THE EYEWITNESS

ERNST WEISS

THE EYEWITNESS

Translated by Ella R. W. McKee

with a Foreword by Rudolph Binion

and a Postscript by Klaus-Peter Hinze

HOUGHTON MIFFLIN COMPANY
BOSTON 1977

Library of Congress Cataloging in Publication Data

Weiss, Ernst, 1882–1940.
   The eyewitness.

   Translation of Ich, der Augenzeuge.
   1. Hitler, Adolf, 1889–1945—Fiction.   I. Title.
pz3.W43733Ey5   [pt2647.E52]   833′.9′12   77–3177
isbn 0–395–25336–5

Printed in the United States of America

v   10   9   8   7   6   5   4   3   2   1

Originally published in German under the title
Der Augenzeuge. © 1963 Kreisselmeier Verlag
KG/Icking bei München

FOREWORD
by Rudolph Binion

THE AFTERMATH of the First World War found Adolf Hitler a charismatic political orator spewing rage and hate. The war itself had seen that same Adolf Hitler an innocuous underling in a front-line Bavarian regiment. The turning point came at the close of the war, when Hitler was hospitalized in Pasewalk for mustard gas poisoning. But mustard gas in and of itself does not work such black magic. What, then, wrought that change in Hitler?

I put this question to a great Hitler scholar, Ernst Deuerlein, one evening in November 1970 as I was beginning to explore that charismatic rage and hate psychohistorically. Deuerlein replied by lending me *Der Augenzeuge* by Ernst Weiss. There just had to be fact behind Weiss's fiction about Hitler at Pasewalk, Deuerlein remarked. That night I read Weiss's central chapter, on the narrator's "miracle cure" of "A.H." in "P." It impressed me in the same way it had impressed Deuerlein before me. True, it echoed a baseless rumor, current in German emigrant circles of the mid-1930s, that some erotic misadventure with a Jewess lay behind Hitler's anti-Semitism. Yet it also explained a piece of Hitler's Pasewalk pathology that was not an issue with German emigrants in the mid-1930s, but that had caught my eye in Hitler's self-versions of the early 1920s: a sickbed hallucination of November 1918. Hitler had half recovered from the temporary blindness induced by his mustard gassing of mid-October 1918 when, as he himself related, the news of the armistice brought on a relapse from which he emerged with a message from above that he would save Germany. This self-account meshed neatly with Weiss's story of the "miracle cure" by hypnotic suggestion through which "A.H." in "P." gains his political calling even as he recovers his eyesight. More, the sequel to this "miracle cure" in the novel turns on "A.H.'s" efforts to round up the related medical papers, among them the informal case notes taken by the psychiatrist at "P." — Weiss's "eyewitness." In point of fact, Hitler really did have his Gestapo seize and destroy every accessible record of his treatment in Pasewalk. Now, Weiss could have known this in the 1930s from no likelier source than the real Pasewalk doctor who had treated Hitler — the original Pasewalk "eyewitness." Who was that Pasewalk doctor?

This was my next question to Deuerlein. He replied that he had been after the answer for a quarter-century, though with little hope of finding it in the absence of those medical records. Our joint efforts had taken us no farther in this particular line when Deuerlein died one year later.

A breakthrough followed early in 1972 when I received a letter from John Toland saying, "This should interest you." Enclosed were Toland's notes on a still-classified 1943 United States Naval Intelligence report on a refugee in Iceland: an Austrian psychiatrist named Karl Kroner. Kroner identified Hitler's Pasewalk doctor as the German psychiatrist Edmund Forster. By Kroner's account, Forster had diagnosed Hitler's complaint of October–November 1918 as psychopathic hysteria and had paid the penalty for this diagnosis by a dubious suicide in September 1933. I promptly scoured Forster's publications for mentions of psychopathic hysteria and spotted one dated 1922: it contained a transparent reference to Hitler in Pasewalk couched in the very language of Weiss's later chapter on "A.H." in "P." Some months later Mona Wollheim, who had typed up the manuscript of *Der Augenzeuge* for Weiss in Paris in 1939 and whom I contacted in New York, drew my attention to a passage in the second edition of Walter Mehring's autobiographical *Die verlorene Bibliothek.* There Mehring related that in the summer of 1933 Hitler's Pasewalk psychiatrist had brought his case records on Hitler to Paris and divulged them to the collaborators on the German emigrant weekly *Das Neue Tage-Buch,* among them Ernst Weiss, before returning to Germany to meet his fate. I checked out *Das Neue Tage-Buch* for the summer of 1933. Sure enough, an editorial of September 1933 on Forster's death mentioned his preceding visit to Paris. It even quoted a remark by him — later requoted in the Mehring reminiscence — in which he enjoined skepticism should his suicide be announced from Germany following his return. To complicate matters, he had emphasized in an article published soon after Hitler's accession that suicide need not be pathological, but might well be the only way out of a tight predicament. As it turns out, his suicide was authentic, fishy as it could well look to anti-Nazis in its time. It followed thirteen days of interrogation after his dismissal as politically unreliable from a chair at the University of Greifswald. During those last thirteen days he told his wife that the Gestapo would even pursue him abroad if he fled. She afterward explained to their elder son that he had once diagnosed Hitler as hysterical. I learned all this, and more, from the university archive in Greifswald and from Forster's elder son in Freiburg im Breisgau in the summer of 1972. The "more" that I learned made it clear that the hero of *Der Augenzeuge* was modeled on Forster point for point in the novelistic sequence, running from the "miracle cure" to the thirteen days of interrogation. This last is the juncture at which Weiss's narrator resists the temptation to commit Forster's suicide. Weiss may have drawn on Forster's case notes directly rather than from memory for the novel's pivotal chapter on the "miracle cure." Mehring told me in 1975 that Forster had made two copies of his Pasewalk records for Leopold Schwarzschild, editor in chief of *Das Neue Tage-Buch*. One of those copies may have gone to Weiss.

My Pasewalk problem was solved. Forster had misdiagnosed Hitler's temporary blindness from mustard gassing as hysterical. Hitler did then suffer a hysterical relapse into blindness at the news of Germany's defeat. Forster cured him by hypnotic suggestion. The message that came through to him from Forster's suggestive therapy was that he would save Germany, but first that he would surmount his physical incapacitation by sheer will power. He set himself up in politics thereafter as a man of will who called on Germans in turn to surmount their own defeat by will power — by a "triumph of the will."

But to solve my Pasewalk problem was to raise Weiss problems galore. The trickiest of these is why Weiss wrote up the Pasewalk story as he did — faithfully in a fictional context (with the transparent abbreviations "A.H." and "P."). Forster's own reason for not telling the Pasewalk story himself appears to have been the same as that of Weiss's narrator: the medical secret. Perhaps, too, Forster was not proud of his misdiagnosis of hysteria (Weiss's narrator is not dogmatic about "A.H.'s" hysteria), let alone his fateful "miracle cure" of an Adolf Hitler. Forster could confide in Weiss while still respecting the medical secret because Weiss was a former doctor. Weiss was the better qualified to be Forster's confidant in the Pasewalk case since Weiss had studied psychoanalysis under Freud while a medical student in Vienna. But was Weiss meant to keep Forster's secret forever? Walter Mehring claims that even after Forster's death *Das Neue Tage-Buch* could not publish the Pasewalk material for fear of trouble from the French authorities. Weiss presumably wrote up Forster's Pasewalk story while it was still fresh in his mind, beginning even before Forster's death, then let it lie for five years before he novelized it in *Der Augenzeuge.* He can hardly have reworked it much when he returned to it. By contrast, it found its way in thick disguise into his *Der arme Verschwender* (*The Poor Spendthrift*), written during that five-year interim. In *Der arme Verschwender,* Forster's "miracle cure" is no stunt of wizardry, but a mere fluke. At the same time it is performed by a narrator who is otherwise wholly identifiable with Weiss himself. Such were Weiss's latent second thoughts about that "miracle cure" he had taken over from Forster for safekeeping.

The narrator in *Der Augenzeuge,* before he comes to "P.," is a self-dramatization of Weiss. Then he is Forster until, after his non-suicide, he enters upon Weiss's own Parisian exile — a world of ever-increasing estrangement and ever-deepening solitude. This autobiographical dimension of Weiss's work documents his sensitive involvement in troubled times. It was along this dimension of novelized eyewitnessing that Weiss's work verged on greatness.

Weiss's life rejoined Forster's in grim actuality as, with France falling to Hitler in June 1940, he killed himself in his turn rather than flee abroad. He had entered his manuscript containing Forster's medical secret in a contest held in America the previous winter for the best novel by a German exile. It survived as a reject. The whereabouts of Forster's original Pasewalk notes and of his later transcriptions is unknown.

CONTENTS

PUBLISHER'S NOTE TO THE ORIGINAL EDITION

THE NOVEL *The Eyewitness* comes from the estate of Ernst Weiss. Errors of the author, which he presumably would have eliminated in an examination of the work, have not been corrected; neither have gaps been closed if such a correction would constitute an encroachment. Mere editorial corrections of the accepted kind have been made.

PART I

FATE DECREED that I should play a special role in the life of one of those people who after World War I created such massive changes and immeasurable suffering in Europe. I have often asked myself what drove me in the fall of 1918 to such an intervention — was it lust for knowledge, the chief characteristic of a researcher in medical science, or was it a desire to act as fate, to be omnipotent, like God himself?

It really does not matter.

But first, I want to present in short sketches, soberly, clearly, unadorned and as far as possible truthfully, my life leading up to that day at the end of October or early November of 1918.

I was born in South Germany as the only legitimate son of a respected engineer in construction. The building of mines and the like had never attracted my father. His real forte was bridges. I remember that he and I with my mother, much loved and delicate, traveled one fall day by train from M. to I.,* and that Father wakened me as we went across a railroad bridge which he had completed the preceding summer. I did not notice anything special about the bridge — one railroad bridge seemed to me to be like all bridges — it crossed over a turbulent stream, with some mossy stones cropping out; the slope, still without any traces of grass, was not especially steep. But my mother acted as if she were really impressed, and she coughed, as she always did when she was excited. My father smiled modestly under his heavy blond mustache. At some time or other he confided in me that it would be even better to build castles, palatial department stores, railroad stations, but he was waiting until later for such an opportunity.

He was always given the title of chief engineer. People bowed deeply to him, but if someone praised his accomplishments, he would turn aside, shake his head in astonishment, and begin to speak, usually of his difficult youth or about his uncle, actually the

* Munich to Innsbruck.

uncle of my mother, who was very wealthy and whose power and influence seemed to be limitless.

I was big for my age, always the strongest in my class. Even then I longed for a friend but never could find one. Probably I could not accept the approaches of classmates for a reason quite common among many children who have no brothers or sisters: I was afraid of the unknown. They, however, were even more fearful of me, of my physical strength, of my silent ways. If they had known that I was especially sensitive to pain, that a harsh word could hurt me as much as a cut, they might have approached me more easily. I could not bear to see anyone suffer — human being or animal — but I rarely cried.

My school was located at the end of a rather broad street in the Meadow Park. One side opened out into the park, or rather to the high wall surrounding it. In the winter, at the beginning of the school day, nothing of the park was visible from the street except the tops of the trees: oaks, plane trees, maples, beech trees. If I surreptitiously looked out of the windows of the schoolroom, lighted by gas lamps, the heavy black branches under their load of snow were at first only faintly visible against the early morning haze. The hum of the gas was cozy, the white-tiled stove gave out warmth, and the pine cones, mixed in the wood and the coal, crackled merrily. The surfaces of the maps and the charts of animals shimmered brightly. About nine or ten o'clock, when the gas lights were extinguished, the maps stopped reflecting; at ten o'clock the room was aired out. The sun had risen, copper red; the mist in the park had been dissipated. With my coat collar turned up and my hands in my pockets, I stood by the windows, now entirely clear, and saw the bushes heavy with frost, the gray-colored skating rink with a thin cover of snow, the great meadow, the smaller meadow in the middle of the park, the tennis courts, surrounded by heavy nets — all deserted. The door opened; the gay tumult of the schoolroom subsided before the teacher had even closed the door behind him.

Not far from this park were the barracks of the Third Cavalry regiment. While we crouched with stooped backs, our heads bent over our notebooks, sleepy from warmth and boredom, and quietly writing out our assignments, we would suddenly hear in a different, faster beat, rhythmic and clear, the sound of the trotting and galloping horses. How often after school I wanted to lean against the thick, wooden, rough barrier in order to watch the riding exercises of the recruits, but this was a forbidden pleasure. Occasionally a soldier approached me — wearing a yellowish white ticking jacket in spite of the cold, on his shorn head a platelike cap without a visor, under his arm a thick, brightly wrapped, crusty loaf of army bread which he wanted to exchange for tobacco or to sell very cheaply. But unfortunately I had neither money nor tobacco. Sadly I watched the cuirassier break the bread into chunks with his powerful hands and feed the pieces to one horse after the other, expertly and without fear. I really do not know why this bread aroused such greed in me. After all, I received everything at home that a sensible child could desire.

One day, however, a soldier must have seen in my eyes this overwhelming longing for some bread. He approached me with clanking spurs and offered me a rather large piece as a present. For a long time afterward I remembered the remarkable acrid odor of leather and tanning which he exuded.

I took the bread, but I did not eat it. At that moment I had decided on a course of action, and I felt compelled to follow it. I gathered my courage together and moved quietly along the fence of the barracks as far as the sentries, only one of whom, the one on the right, noticed me. To his shout I answered that I had to visit the sick son of a corporal who lived in the barracks. I slipped into the entrance and found myself in the courtyard. I saw several horses, three I think, who were hitched together and who were stomping on the hard, dusty earth and switching their long tails. I gave the horse nearest me a piece of bread; I was cold with fear but flushed with joy and happiness that I had accomplished my desire to prove my courage. Whether my hand trembled or whether the horse did not want the crust and rejected it I do not know, but in any case the bread fell to the ground. In spite of an acute consciousness of certain danger I bent down; the blood rushed to my head so that I did not see the bread under the many restless hooves. The horses, whom the stableboys had left alone for a few minutes, were waiting for their midday feeding and were fidgety. They were well trained, waiting for the trumpet signal. They pulled one against the other; I could hear how the bridles crunched. I could not stand up; I twisted around on the ground, between the twelve hooves, found the bread, felt that I was safe, and straightened up. Just then one of the horses – I think the same one to whom I had offered the delicacy – too eager to obey the trumpet signal, stepped on me. It was the first really unbearable pain of my life. I heard myself groan and then I fainted, but not into painlessness. I was not conscious; nonetheless I was very much aware of the horrible pain. Fortunately, the hoof had glanced off my schoolbag, smashing a heavy ruler. I came to in a commons, screaming in pain until I had no more breath, my knapsack under my head, a horse blanket at my feet. The pain burned in my back; I could not breathe, but I had to scream; otherwise I would die, I was sure. The soldiers stood around me, most of them watching me thoughtfully and irritably. One of them bent down to ask me a question, but I could not talk. My address was in my books, and I motioned with my hand to my schoolbag. A cuirassier, embarrassed, took it out from under my head, opened a book and read syllable by syllable like a schoolboy my name and address. Suddenly they all stood at attention; the doctor entered and ordered them to be at ease. Their faces, which had been ceremoniously expressionless as if they were in church, relaxed. They lifted me up, I groaned and everything went black, but I did not faint again as I had hoped.

While the doctor examined me, probing and listening, I was overcome by a feeling of destruction. As a young person I had so little idea of death that I thought of everything else but the fact that it could be my last moment. Perhaps the pain was too oppressive, too shattering, too choking for such thoughts. Each breath was like a bolt of lightning in my right side. When I tried to hold my breath, it was less painful, but as soon as I had to breathe deeply in order to avoid suffocating, the same self-induced pain was even more unbearable. Groaning and panting made it worse, so I forced myself to a dogged silence and earned the respectful approval of the doctor, who murmured something about a young Spartan.

The military doctor evidently did not view my hurt as serious; otherwise he would have kept me in his little hospital instead of letting me go home in a small military coach under the care of a mustached corporal. Perhaps the torture during the trip home would have been more bearable in the doctor's company, since he had sympathized with me and had rewarded me with his respect for my self-control. All the corporal wanted was to deliver me as soon as possible. When the wagon rolled especially fast over the cobblestones, I reached for his hand, but he must have misunderstood the gesture, for he urged the cuirassier to go still faster, maybe out of fear that I might die in the wagon and cause the regiment unpleasantness.

I was furious when I realized that I had come into this difficult situation because of my good nature. I seethed with rage at the thought of the ungrateful horse which had repaid my friendliness with a heavy kick. I lay on my left side because breathing was easier for me there, but my handkerchief was in the pocket of my coat on that side; when I moved a little to reach it so that I could wipe the saliva from my mouth, a feeling of disintegration came over me again, a choking, ghastly loathing, and I sank once more into oblivion.

When I again saw clearly, I realized that we were on our street but that he had driven past our apartment house. I had great difficulty trying to convince the stupid soldier that he was mistaken about the number and that I really knew where I lived. Every word was painful — and I had to use many. Finally we stopped in front of our house. He picked me up, complaining about my weight, and dragged me up the steps so awkwardly that my feet trailed behind. Not until we stood in the entrance did it occur to me how frightened my mother would be.

My mother was very delicate. I hoped that she would not open the door but rather that the maid or my father — but she was there. When she saw me, she cried softly and collapsed, with her head outside the door so that she fell on the foot scraper with the word "Welcome" on it. The stupid cuirassier with me in his arms did not know what to do. Fortunately my father appeared; he saw the difficulty and helped my mother to rise, led her into her room and told her that I was in no danger. He laid me carefully on my bed. In passing, he told the maid to stay with my mother and not to let her out of her room. But in two or three minutes she came anyhow, tottering on the arm of the maid, and sat down on the bed. She took off my shoes first, then my clothes. She did it all so gently that the pain was not intensified. I had no bandage and I did not bleed. Since she did not change my shirt, she did not see my crushed side. She shook her head; I was not to talk. She coughed and held me firmly with both hands as if I wanted to escape. My father had hurried off to telephone our family doctor. He came back shortly with the report that the doctor had been home and would come to us soon. Then he took the corporal into the next room and both began to smoke while the mustached soldier gave my father an incorrect report of the accident, which he had not witnessed. My mother was crying more and more, so that my bed shook. She was most sympathetic; she overwhelmed me with endearments as she had done in my earliest days, she petted me, she wanted me to lie more comfortably, she offered me everything imaginable. She thought that by these means she would lighten my pain, but actually she had the opposite effect. I began to feel very sorry for myself; my heart became more and more constricted in my wounded chest as I thought of what a poor, unfortunate child I was. I felt better when the sensible Jewish doctor appeared. He smelled of medicine and was dressed in a grease-spotted frock-coat. He examined me only casually and asked me several questions: had I urinated, had I spit up blood? I shook my head. He insisted that I must relieve myself. He asked my mother to leave and he helped me. He advised me to be patient and then went into the next room to report. Shortly they all reentered my room, all trying to talk at once, crowding the little room and taking all the oxygen. All were reconciled in one way or another to my accident and were happy that it had not been worse. My father and the corporal smoked. I could not understand that no one considered that I might not be able to bear such pain for a long time, but no one thought of it except my mother, who lay useless compresses on my forehead.

I will not describe that afternoon, evening or night. Only someone who has experienced something similar can sympathize. Comforting words are only irritating and do not help. My mother must have realized that. Never did a hand rest more lightly on a sore chest than hers did as she fell asleep in the gray of dawn. But I bore it just as I had borne everything else, regardless of how desperate I was. And just as I could never have imagined such pain, just so I could not conceive that it would ever end. But it seemed to me that it had not yet achieved its peak, and several times a tickle struck me as it does before one sneezes.

As long as I was awake, I had sufficient strength to withstand this frightening tickle. The doctor had warned me to cough as little as possible, to avoid talking, and to refrain from tossing in bed. At that time — not even fifteen hours had passed since then, and yet it seemed to me that it had been another life which would never return, so beautiful — I had not really understood this warning. Why should I cough? Why should I be restless in bed? But in the early morning hours, as my mother, sunk together in the old wingbacked chair, breathed more and more deeply in her quiet sleep, both hands, gentle with blue veins, lying in her lap, I was sorely tempted to yield to these desires.

I was particularly eager to change my position. I lay on my right side, on five broken ribs and on the bruised muscles. After I had gradually turned myself, using all kinds of stratagems, and lay on the healthy side, I immediately had difficulty breathing. Then I tried lying on my back. But the injured side, which could breathe more freely, hurt so much that I hit the pillow. So I went back to the right side. This great effort made me break out in a sweat, and I was overcome by such weariness that it seemed to me I had again become a very little child. I yielded; I slept. I do not know of what I dreamed. Suddenly a new dream of terrible horror broke into the old dream, which had been pleasant and leisurely. I noticed how someone tickled me with a sharp, pointed knife. I felt as though fire burned through me. I sat up laughing in indescribable fright and the knife cut through me again and again. I can still see it — it was like a knife which is used for carving a hen, sharpened on both edges, thin, very smooth and long. I awoke. I sat upright; the pillows had been thrown on the carpet. It was beginning to get light at the windows, but the rest of the room was dark. My mother was gone. I screamed for help, and as I screamed, something bitter and salty rose in my throat. I clung to the brass rods of the bed and shook them. My mother rushed into the room with a burning light, half-dressed, barefoot, her hair hanging in long curls around her shoulders. She embraced me with her arms still damp from washing and pulled her nightgown up around her neck. My eyelids touched her lukewarm smooth neck, and I felt the veins beating. Suddenly the bitter, salty something forced itself through my lips, and I could not stop it. The horrible, foamy, bright red blood appeared on the embroidered edges of her nightgown. Strangely, the thought of death still had not occurred to me. But not so for her. As soon as she saw the spots of blood, she loosened my hands and ran to my father, telling him to go immediately for the priest with the sacrament and then to the doctor. I heard him get out of the creaking bed, struggle with his clothes and shoes. Blood continued to flow into my mouth.

My mother was with me again. As a devout Catholic, she was more concerned about my eternal salvation than about my life. What better could she do for me than to hold me in her arms, pray, and make vows? She did not expect me in this hour of death to pray aloud with her. In fact, she said that I should be quiet; she pushed me into a recumbent position, piled up the pillows at my back without a break in her praying, fetched several of her little handkerchiefs scented with vanilla, dabbed the perspiration from my forehead, the blood from my mouth, and the tears from my eyes. In a soft voice she vowed to make a pilgrimage to the Holy Mother of God in Altötting if I should have relief from the pain and the bleeding.

I would have felt better if she had been quiet and had let me sit up and hold tightly to the rods of the bed. For now something new had come over me; perhaps I could best call it a monster, crushing, grinding, consuming. It had no connection with the earlier pain. It resembled most the moment when the horse's hoof had broken my right side after gliding down my knapsack and breaking my ruler — that is, the very first moment.

This feeling lasted maybe a quarter of an hour or a half-hour. I cannot judge accurately. Without having noticed that I had been absent, I found myself again when the doctor entered.

My father held a hasty conversation with my mother. He was much less devout than she, and so he had not yet gone to the priest. He wanted to hear the decision of the doctor first and see what help he could give. The doctor did not listen long to my groaning. He put his finger, which smelled of almond soap, across my lips as if to encourage my silence; then he took out of the tails of his grease-flecked frockcoat a case padded with purple velvet which contained a little nickel syringe and a small bottle of ether, the smell of which stimulated me to renewed heavy coughing. Out of another pocket he took a little bottle on which were printed the word *morphine* and a skull with two crossed shinbones. These seemed to me, however, to be a symbol of comfort. I cared about nothing — only that the pain should be in the past. I felt easier in his presence, and if one can speak of being happy under such circumstances, I was happy that he had come as the first one to help me rather than the priest. The doctor had pushed up the sleeve of my nightshirt, cleansed the skin with ether, drawn up the morphine, and let a little stream of liquid rise from the syringe; then he stuck the needle expertly into my arm and, after a second, withdrew it. Then he sat down by me and looked out the window, his features tense, silent, bleary-eyed. He yawned behind his thin, slender hand.

A peculiar feeling of relief crept over me. Not that the pain vanished at once. On the contrary, it continued and was with me for a long time, even though diminished in intensity. But a calming reassurance lay like a dressing with good ointment over the pain, a veil, softness, silence, yawning, the gradual brightening of the room. My mother came in, with bright red spots on her cheeks, wearing a dark dress. She was astounded by the sudden change which she saw in me. She could not conceive that the little, unprepossessing doctor had accomplished it. He pulled out his watch, held it to his ear to be sure that it was still running, and counted my pulse. The room was bright by then, but it seemed strange to me. I saw everything clearly but as if from a distance; I was present but at the same time crossing a bridge. I noticed how the others talked to each other, but I did not understand them. Somebody wiped some moisture from my mouth. The cloth remained white — it must have been winter.

This miracle was unforgettable for me; perhaps it was the determining factor in my decision to become a doctor. My father's bridges left me cold. Military life, which had formerly intrigued me, was now obnoxious. The miracle made everything clear to me.

It had nothing to do with the good Dr. Kaiser, rather the opposite. My parents had him come again and again, but they considered him only a necessary evil. Sometimes they went so far in their denigration of him that they opened the windows and aired out the room after he left — not because he spread an unpleasant odor but because he was a Jew. My mother had an aversion to every Jew, although she knew only a few and knew nothing really blameworthy about any of them. Perhaps it was her Catholic upbringing, for she did not care for Lutherans either, whom she considered cunning.

There was in our town a second Dr. Kaiser, a very thin, tall, proud, rich man, who had built a large, self-contained sanatorium for the nervous and the insane. In S.,* a little place on a long, beautiful lake where we owned a little wooden cottage with a small orchard, he had a magnificent villa built of marble with panes of plate glass and a terrace that was built out over the water. He almost never walked in town; he usually rode in a carriage drawn by his two dapple-gray horses with one of his children on the back seat, but next to him sat a beautiful young woman. Later he was one of the first to own an automobile. Our family doctor was known as Kaiser-Jew; the other one, whom everyone greeted ceremoniously with tipped hat, was called scornfully the Fool's Kaiser.

In the days following the miracle, I was often delirious and I grew very thin. I thought a great deal about the superior power of a doctor. If even an unprepossessing, fat Kaiser-Jew possessed such a power, how immeasurable must be the power of someone like the Fool's Kaiser!

It was not only the sudden, magical effect of the medicine in the bottle with the skull. Whenever I was plagued by pain and shortness of breath, the Kaiser-Jew did not need to do anything more than to enter my room, and I would breathe more easily in the truest sense of the word, and the sharp pains in my lungs were blown away.

Sensitivity to pain had always been my weakest point. My school comrades would never have believed that, but I knew it all too well. There is a very effective means for withdrawing from pain, for example, in the case of the brutal fights among boys in which every tear, every whimper counts as a disgrace. This means of withdrawal is cowardice. I was somewhat cowardly; that was why I held aloof as often as possible from all games. Games and fighting are almost the same for boys. My comrades saw only that I was

* Starnberg.

big for my age, that I had hard muscles and little fat and strong bony hands — "hams." They could not imagine that a sensitive nature inhabited such a powerful body. I was unable to see not only my own sufferings without agony, but also those which hurt others; it grieved me, the tears appeared, and I was ashamed.

Perhaps everything would have been different if I had had sisters and brothers. We would have hardened each other and would have been gay. My mother often mentioned that she would present me with a little sister, or maybe two or three, twins or triplets. She would say it laughing while she was coughing or coughing while she was laughing, for she was really delicate. My father did not like such talk and considered it immodest that she wanted to be smarter than God himself, who fortunately, in light of her delicate health, had left them with but a single child. Then my mother would be angry again, circles of red would appear on her cheeks, and she would tell my father to be quiet since such comments were not fit for my ears.

Once I was nailed, as it were, to my bed, a new spirit appeared in me which provided me with a kind of satisfaction or substitute for my lost boyish pleasures — that is, the will to rule over those who were important, to make my ideas a reality among those who were mighty. I began with the doctor. He helped me. As long as he sat by me, my chest moved more easily, my pains were gone. He examined me often and thoroughly, for the fever, which was never high but which never disappeared, caused him concern. He would find nothing serious and would therefore be ready to leave after five or ten minutes. There is no trick that I did not use to circumvent him and to keep him there another minute. When he recognized my unskillful maneuvers, I besought my mother and then my father to help keep him there longer. They paid him a double fee, they talked with him about something interesting, and sometimes they actually succeeded in getting him to hang up his black fur hat, glimmering with all kinds of colors, on the brass window catch and to spread out the tails of his grease-spotted frockcoat and to sit down again on the bed. It may be that he then neglected other important patients. It is possible that he simply was granting me this satisfaction.

At night I slept restlessly; I often perspired, and my father, who had more faith in the doctor than my mother, urged him to try more energetic measures. My mother preferred to leave everything in the hands of the Virgin, who had always helped her in her weakness.

The doctor was quite willing to cooperate. One day he brought all kinds of instruments in a shabby case. He took out a syringe which was much larger and looked much more threatening than the one he had used for my miraculous cure. "Are you a brave little fellow?" he asked, laying his finger again on my mouth. I anticipated nothing good. I thought of the brave little Spartan of the doctor in the barracks.

Besides, an entirely false report of my adventure was current. I had actually wanted to give bread to the horses. I had never excited them with blows with my ruler, as that corporal, the false witness, had reported to my parents. I was not motivated by kindness or sympathy for the well-fed, plump, heavy horses. I had merely wanted to conquer my cowardice, to put my courage to the test, for, like many city children, I was afraid of horses, particularly of their hooves and their teeth. I had stood the test but paid dearly for it. Should that not be enough?

Then I was sorry that I had so often delayed the doctor, that I, a little, helpless, bedridden boy, had sought to dominate him. But what good did it do? I clenched my teeth together. I held my breath. Holding my breath has always been a means for protecting myself against pain or of relieving pain. If only the doctor had courageously gone ahead! But he looked for a long time for the best place, he pressed carefully here and there, he tapped and listened and tickled me horribly. It was the highest time when he finally plunged the hollow needle between my ribs. I did not cry out. That night I did not sleep. I considered myself a rare, an unusual person who was untouched by pain.

I forgot to report that the Kaiser-Jew had suggested that he would give me a little ether if I thought that I could not endure the operation, but my ignorance about ether frightened me more than the thought of pain. I made myself strong and I had been strong.

I was very much helped by this little painful operation which the doctor called the next day "a wonderfully successful pleural tap." My fever sank as if by magic to the delight of my mother, who honored the doctor that day with an extra honorarium of a golden twenty-mark coin from her household money. He accepted it, perspiring and blushing — it was very hot that day. Two days later I was allowed to get up, and soon I went outside, and then to school, where I was the object of great admiration.

I was proud of my recovery. After some thought I realized that the tap, which had removed some yellowish-red liquid from the chest cavity, would have been successful even if I had not behaved so bravely. But I had been brave. I had not even stirred. I had doubly proved my courage — first when I had incurred the danger of being trodden underfoot by a pack of wild horses (that was my view then), and again when I accepted the unusually severe pains with extraordinary composure and self-control. I said again and again to myself: I can do what I want to. I was radiant with inner joy and pride. In fact, my ambition in school was also awakened. I had always been just an average, mediocre pupil; then, however, I studied assiduously without any urging (my father was much astonished) and made up in a short time all the material which had been covered during my illness. That too was a source of pride.

The doctor had grown fond of me, but I did not need him anymore. He came occasionally, sat down at the table with me, and talked to me. I discovered that his wife was dead and that he lived with his daughter, Victoria. I imagined her to be an oldish, dried-up spinster. One day, shortly before the beginning of summer vacation, I passed by the girls' school. The Kaiser-Jew was waiting in front of the gate with his shabby instrument case under his arm; he was dressed in a somewhat faded, light blue, shiny jacket instead of his old frockcoat. As the school bell stopped ringing, a beautiful, slender, honey-blond young girl in a white ankle-length crocheted dress went up to him. He took a sheet of paper from her hand and beamed with pride and joy. It was his daughter, who had just passed her final examinations with brilliant marks.

I had become especially attached to my mother during my illness. I recognized with a clear insight that I had always loved her — but my illness had changed me and she had changed, too. Not that she overflowed with caresses and tender words, but she did something that she had always avoided: she began to adorn herself for me. She bought the most beautiful things that she could. She especially desired expensive ornaments; she often stood, coughing softly, in front of the jeweler's window, and her bright black-cherry eyes would go from the brooches and bracelets to a double strand of pearls and back again. Her arm, which she had in mine, as if she needed protection, began to tremble slightly, and she went on very reluctantly. I loved her not as something strange, like a second person, but I loved her as I loved myself. She and I overflowed into each other without a break. I saw her and felt her alongside me even when I was alone. That did not make me dreamy and soft; rather, it made me daring, certain of myself. The drive to dominate which had developed during my experience of pain and suffering had not diminished after my recovery, but I did not attempt to practice it on her as I sometimes did with my father, occasionally with success, occasionally without. She and I were too much one person.

Vacation time was near at hand; my father assumed that we would go to S. I would have liked that best, too, and the doctor was in favor of it. My mother, however, had other plans. When I had been in danger, she had made the vow to make a pilgrimage to Altötting, and she wanted to fulfill this vow. I was to accompany her. Every year, especially in the fall after the harvest, there were great processions to the miracle-working shrine of the Virgin, in which, as a rule, peasant women participated. They wore their black silk skirts hiked up high, pitch-black straw hats with long narrow streamers falling over their bony, sun-browned faces. Everyone, old and young, rich and poor, plodded through the dust of the roads in rank and file, singing litanies in chorus with the priest who led them onward as they piously fingered their rosaries. Directly behind the priest there was sometimes a small number of women from the cities as well as a few gentlemen, sedately dressed and older. My mother could have joined them. She would have attempted that kind of exertion for herself, but not for me. Actually, she was now much weaker and more susceptible than I. She came up with the idea of renting a coach and going on foot only part of the way each day. When I could go no farther, the coach would carry us on. She told my father nothing of her plan; we discussed it secretly while he slept.

Since, however, it rained almost steadily, we walked very little.

In spite of that, my mother arrived at the shrine completely exhausted, her teeth chattering from chills and fever. Most of the inns were occupied, but we finally found a little room. Then I was the one who was awake at her bedside. I could not take my eyes off her. She was so beautiful. Sometimes in her fever she looked younger and more fetching than the honey-blond Victoria.

I never prayed for myself, only for her. After two days of chills and fever, she suddenly stood up in good spirits and made the last part of the pilgrimage without any difficulty, even though it was along a steep path on which the Stations of the Cross were portrayed in wooden pictures. In the evening we fasted, on the next day we received the sacrament, and then we ran to the station lest we miss the train. We rode to S., where Father was waiting for us, laughing, with flowers in his hand. My mother remained somewhat serious. It began to rain softly, and the roof of our cottage, weighted down with heavy stones, glistened in the rain.

During the first days there was almost uninterrupted rain. I slept much and ate enough for three. I was not permitted to swim, so I did not suffer from the bad weather as I would have if I could have gone into the water. My mother was quiet; she was concerned about me. I radiated health and joy in life. I would have liked to tear out trees, to run around the entire lake without stopping, to barrel down the mountain meadow, my head between my shoulders, my arms around my knees, curled up in a ball. My mother was patient with me, very patient.

But she was no longer the same — maybe because of the long stay in the little village at the end of the lake which she had never really liked; maybe because of boredom, her lack of customary activity or the fact that she could do very little more for me. Ill-tempered, she sat in her resplendent new clothes at the window, coughed and looked out, shivering. I had never been very communicative; so now, when I tried to be, I achieved nothing. My mother gently stroked my hair with a distraught expression and managed a subdued smile. She often looked at herself in her mirror. It almost seemed as if she were making an effort to laugh less, to speak less. When I in my childish way, certainly without any real talent for it, wanted to cheer her up, her features, usually so gentle, became distorted. It was as if she had the impulse down in her chest or up in her throat to cough, then she would hold her hand over her mouth as if she were commanding herself to be quiet.

In spite of the unfavorable weather, my father made little day trips into the mountains and returned in the best of moods in his loden clothes steaming with dampness. He would have a rare flower such as could be found in the heights decorating his Tyrolean hat. My mother accepted his kisses patiently. Afterward, however, I saw how she dried off her mouth with one of her little batiste handkerchiefs and overcame only with great effort a particularly strong compulsion to cough. I thought that she had wiped off her lips because my father's mouth and beard were so wet from the rain. Only much later did I begin to understand. In any case, this did not happen very often.

One day after a foggy morning the sun appeared, the mists disappeared, and the lake had great blue-gray waves, glistening silver here and there. The wind was harsh and strong. By afternoon it was so dry that we could drink our coffee out in the open under one of the neglected apple trees which were already full of small apples, hard as rocks and poison-green. These apples never got ripe and sweet; they ripened in a way but were never edible. Even the housewifely arts of my mother failed; she had wanted to make a kind of sauce by adding enormous quantities of sugar. I stayed with her on this beautiful day although I was sorely tempted to go to the village, to the lake, into the woods or to the moor — it really made no difference where. Joy of life and enthusiasm pounded in every vein. I had been restricted to my bed for months, finally I was well; only a thick, but painless hard lump on the right side of my back showed where the horse had hurt me. I spent the next day also with my mother, perturbed by her pallor and weariness. Together we stretched an old, somewhat torn hammock with creaking hemp ropes between an apple tree and an ancient pear tree which had long since stopped bearing.

We made a real effort to follow the injunctions of my father about not injuring the bark with the ropes. My mother lay down as best she could. But since the one side of the hammock was lower and her head lay way down, I went to fetch a pillow out of her bedroom while she was sleeping somewhat restlessly. When I raised the bedspread and picked up the pillows, a crumpled batiste handkerchief fell out. It showed traces of dark blood. I realized at once what it meant, and the monster, grinding, crushing, consuming, overwhelmed me again.

I did not want my mother to realize that I knew why she had changed so much. I straightened her snow-white pillows and covers so well that in the evening she did not notice that anyone had disturbed her bed. I returned without a pillow. She was awake again and seemed to be impatient. I no longer attempted to discover what she so steadfastly kept to herself, surely because of her love for me. She was worried about her life. She had always had weak lungs, and the concern about me had hurt her. I went even further. When she urged me to make use of the beautiful weather and go swimming (she had momentarily forgotten that it was forbidden), I yielded and acted as if I could not contain my joy. She wanted that. She wanted to be alone; perhaps she thought that complete rest and pious prayers were the best life for her.

My father at that time was enjoying himself by learning to row. Of course he had always known how to row an ordinary boat, but what intrigued him then was to row one of the fishermen's boats, which were several meters long, clumsy, flat, and wooden. This is done from the stern with a flat wooden log which one sets in a turning movement; the oarsman must use the weight of his entire body to accomplish it. At first my father did not move from the spot, to the good-natured amusement of the fishermen and the young girls on the shore; in fact the boat, which is called a flatboat there, came back to shore. But since he was very powerful and apt, he soon developed the technique. On my mother's saint's day he persuaded her to sit in a flatboat decorated with Chinese lanterns hanging from wires, with me at her feet, and ride to the little city of T.* I was afraid that the damp air of the lake would hurt her, but to my surprise she seemed to feel better and hardly coughed at all. The serious, withdrawn expression of her face, which previously had appeared so childlike, was still there. It did not fit with the very beautiful new silk dress and the narrow golden brooch which she wore to celebrate the day. My father sang on the way home; she and I remained silent. Soon afterward she put the new clothes into her trunk and never wore them again.

* Tutzing.

The next day I was drawn to the moor. The end of the lake consisted of pebbled earth which became flatter and flatter; it was overgrown with reeds, around which the awkward steamboat made a wide circuit. On the other side of the broad highway which went around the lake there was still another area, not solid ground but also not water; one merged with the other. A few small lakes called the Oster Lakes, rich with fish but bottomless and dangerous, glistened in the pale, dull green landscape. There were narrow footpaths through the area, in which there was no habitation far and wide. Just on the edge, where it began to rise, a few miserable huts of peatcutters stood. Everything there was different from the lakeshore — the plants were more luxuriant, the unknown birds more frightful, with gayer feathers, the butterflies bigger, but it seemed less shy. Even the air shimmered differently in the summer heat than over the meadows, the fields, the open water. I tried to catch a butterfly with sapphire-colored wings that seemed very sluggish. I followed after him, often jumping over soft places or small rills. Old wooden posts with moldy bundles of hay showed points of danger here and there, but these were really very scattered. The ground, spongy under my feet, lured me on. Finally, with patience and trickery, I succeeded in capturing the butterfly under my hat. Then I thought that I would have to grasp it roughly if I wanted to keep it, and I realized that that would be a shame — so the butterfly flew away, moving its jewel-colored wings silently. But when I wanted to return, I found that there was nothing around me but moor. From the village I heard in the loneliness and quiet the well-known tones of the tower clock striking six. It was still early, and it seemed to be brighter. What I had thought was twilight had been only a cloud which had moved in front of the sun. I tried again to get out of the moor. If only I knew how I had come! I had jumped, throwing my hat over the butterfly; in the meantime the traces of my spiked shoes had been entirely wiped out by the gurgling ground, and wherever I attempted to step, I sank in.

I heard voices, laughter and yodeling, but I could see no one. All over were shrubs, alders and willows, high reeds in bloom, gorse and grass. Moor and land mixed up, interlaced with little paths. Wild birds flew up, green and blue-gold spots on their rich feathers and wings. Frogs croaked and crickets sang in chorus nearby. I called for help but was too ashamed to call very loud. I took off my shoes, took their laces in my hand, and experimented whether I could get more easily over the spots covered with deceptive green with bare feet. I breathed deeply; the bitter smell of the moor, the peat and hot grass was everywhere. But I made the mistake, which I discovered later, that most people do in a similar situation. At first I had been too bold, too daring; then I was too cautious. I stood on one leg instead of jumping ahead with both feet. Besides, my bare feet gave me an unpleasant, tickling feeling. When I noticed with cold fright that the one leg bearing the burden of my body was sinking, slowly but surely, centimeter by centimeter, into the gurgling ground, I naturally tried to stand on the other foot and to free the first one. This succeeded, however, only to the extent that the second sank deeper into the doughlike, gurgling moor. Thus a person who is ignorant sinks deeper and deeper into the morass.

The laughing and shouting had grown more distant. The people could certainly not be very far away. But on the other hand, maybe so, for the air could carry the sound very far: I heard the cows low, and they were pastured in a meadow at the edge of the forest at least a half-hour from where I stood. Exercising great self-control, I gave up the attempt to get out by myself. I sat down and calmed myself until the pains in the broken ribs diminished. I took my stockings out of the pocket of my jacket and pulled them up on my black, sticky legs. While I was busy doing that, several people and some dogs on a leash suddenly appeared. It was the Fool's Kaiser with his three boys. He and his oldest son carried guns on their shoulders, but only he had some game, a wild duck I think, in his hunting bag. The green and blue-gold speckled neck and the head with the yellow beak hung out. Blood dripped from its beak. They moved quietly forward on solid ground. I jumped up, following them, and I found myself on solid, hard, good ground just as they, who had no idea of what this jump had meant for me.

The little footpath led between bushes not over five meters away from the little island in the moor. I could have recognized the direction long before by the warning post standing there. But once again I had sought danger and then had been as lost as if I had been blind. Ashamed, I trotted along behind Kaiser and his boys back to the village. The second oldest son, a very handsome boy but somewhat shy, seemed to like me. His cheeks were covered with fine down and he blushed easily. When he smiled at me, he showed his beautiful teeth. We had known each other for years, since his family, like mine, came here every year. At first he stuttered, but he soon was composed. We trailed behind his father and brothers and let them follow their path into the woods with the dogs who were continually barking. We went directly to my garden gate. Whenever it was opened, an old, rusty, hoarse bell resounded. My mother came from the house toward us, giving my guest an unfriendly, probing look. I invited him to sit down at the table where plates of fruit were set out, and later, to lie down in the hammock. I wanted to offer him something, to play the host. But my mother's mien became ever colder; he noticed it and took his departure with an awkward, clumsy bow since he had a piece of a big sour apple still in his mouth. My mother responded icily with an equally awkward nod of her head. I was so embarrassed that I forgot to ask him if I could see him again. But the next day, as I was reading some of Andersen's fairy tales aloud to my mother, I saw him stroll by our house with one of his father's dogs on a leash. My mother resented the interruption of my reading. She threw me my hat, which lay on the sofa, stood up, and almost pushed me out of the garden — I should not lose a minute; I should stay away as long as I felt like and amuse myself wherever I pleased. I hesitated, but nothing helped.

And just that morning I had made a firm resolve to please her and to amuse her, since the evening before remained as a dark memory. Not because of Helmut Kaiser — for my mother had always wished that I would associate more with those of my own age — but because of something else. Thoughtlessly I had undressed and become aware of the sticky moor dirt on my feet. I had tiptoed out of the room, hoping not to awaken my mother, who had fallen asleep over her handwork. I had fetched a wooden bucket from the kitchen, filled it at the well, and set it on a chair in order to wash my feet. I was almost done when I noticed my mother looking at me penetratingly. If only she had asked! If only she had scolded me! If only she had given me a slap on my cheek as she had sometimes laughingly done in the past! It would have hurt less than this silent glance, whose meaning I understood too well. It said, "You have done it again. Without thinking of how disturbed I become, you had to go to the forbidden moor. You sank in it, and God only knows who pulled you out so that you were not destroyed as so many others have been. You were not satisfied with your stupid adventure with the horse which caused your father and me such concern and which took its toll of my health!" She said nothing. She coughed as I had not heard her cough since that first evening after our arrival in Altötting, and she pressed her handkerchief to her pale, stern-looking mouth. I ran with bare feet over the plain floor to her; I wanted to kiss her hand or put my forehead on her neck as I had done when the blood had poured out of my lungs. But she did not move. Nothing stopped me. But I went back unkissed and uncaressed. I carried the bucket with the dirty water so awkwardly out of the room that the water spilled out. I lay awake a long time that night. My father came home late. As the owner of property, he had been included in a little dancing party among the citizens of S. He sang softly to himself, something he did only rarely.

I thought to myself in the quiet of the night that maybe the second son of Dr. Kaiser would be my friend. His shyness came from the fact that his high and mighty father and his two brothers always treated him with condescension. The eldest had the birthright and greater physical strength; the youngest was the favorite, coddled child. Only Helmut had nothing special. He had learned to live with this knowledge. His father had a heavy hand when he punished. I tried to teach Helmut my secret for lessening pain, holding my breath. He had another method: he counted backward from one hundred down.

He told me exciting things — and for a boy of my age, incomprehensible things — about his father's patients. The most ghastly, however, was what he said about the dogs, who were now on vacation from his father's "clinical jail." They had been captured on the street by warders and had not been claimed by their owners. They were destined for painful experiments, about the purpose and end of which we had no concept. Among these dozens of dogs there were always several hunting dogs, which his father brought

23

out into the country at the beginning of the vacation, gave them a few weeks of respite, and then relinquished them to their dreadful fate. I considered it dreadful; it did not seem so to the phlegmatic Helmut. At the same time he was warmhearted, spoke much of his mother and his two brothers, even shed something like a tear at his departure and promised to write. He and his brothers were not being reared by their father but by their mothers. Each son had a different mother, each of whom lived in a different city. His father was then married to his fourth wife.

At the end of August the weather turned bad again. In fact, it began to snow at the beginning of September. My mother bitterly blamed my father as if he were responsible for the bad weather; she spoke with a deliberately soft voice emphasizing her weakness. He answered by suggesting in sport that she should pack the trunks. He was astonished the next morning to discover that they were packed and that the porter was at the garden entrance with his little green cart, ready to take them to the station. Throughout the summer my father had been even-tempered and happy, quite comradely with me. We had had long conversations about Kaiser-Jew and the Fool's Kaiser and also about the lovely Jewish princess, Victoria.

My mother was somewhat improved. She was still very serious and almost never laughed. Once I had poked around in the dirty laundry, even though it was repulsive, to see if any bloody handkerchiefs were there. My guilty conscience troubled me. When I saw that there was nothing like that, I felt better again.

In the time following, my life was devoted on the one hand to school and learning, fighting and making peace, football and handball and whatever else occupied a healthy boy of my age surrounded by comrades, including reading adventure stories and collecting stamps, which Helmut had encouraged me to undertake; and on the other hand to the worry about my mother. Why did she not understand it? I could not really be with her day and night, could I? Once I had been a part of her, she said one time. But she did not want to explain it to me, and I did not inquire further, at least not at that time and not from her. (I learned it later from my comrades in a coarse way.)

I did not know if I was still a part of her since her health did not return quickly, but she remained one with me. I had a good childhood; I say that even now. I was always healthy; the severe damage caused by the ungrateful horse had healed without any after-effects. But the following winter she made a remark with a peculiar bitterness which was hard to understand. She compared my quick recovery to her slow, hesitant and even painful illness. I was the cause of my misfortune; I had deliberately exposed myself, but she had not. And she was devout, much more so than either my father or I. Yet heaven was trying her so bitterly; the pilgrimage to Altötting had been fruitless. (Did she do it on my account or on hers?) And in her present condition she could not make another; she would not get there even in a closed carriage.

I could do nothing but pat her hands. But they were damp, and she dried off mine as if I had dirtied them on hers. I did not understand it — or I understood it only too well! I surmised each of her thoughts. She did not need to say anything. But that did not make our lives any easier.

Seemingly she left me entirely free. But she did not like it if I took advantage of that freedom. In these adolescent years, alongside this love or perhaps just because of this love, I had an insatiable need to be free, to move about, to be alone. In my free time I had an irresistible urge to wander alone through the city and its environs. On these walks I did not forget my mother, who, in the meantime, lay on the sofa in the one really sunny room of our house, in her hands some handwork which was never finished. On a small table near her was the thermometer with which she was supposed to take her temperature every three hours. On the contrary, during these wanderings I was with my mother but in a different way, much more intimate and sweet, as it had happened a few times between us. When I was alone with my thoughts of her in the streets, on the fields, by the river, or in the woods, I loved her most deeply and I was happiest. I tried once to explain this to her. She had me repeat it three times, then she shook her head and compressed her lips, which became even paler and more wrinkled. She did not want to hear. It was useless.

But I understood that she did not struggle so much with me as with her illness. The doctor was often in our house. He advised her to go to a sanatorium where he guaranteed she would be completely cured in two or three months, for her case was favorable and she was past the critical age of thirty years. She smiled but really more scornfully than confidently. Afterward she remarked that the Jewish doctor always used such low, commercial terms as "guarantee" and that he was so proud of the youth of his daughter, Victoria, that he calculated my mother's age, something a Christian doctor would never do. And even though I was fond of the doctor and his daughter, my mother convinced me, and I did not feel as kindly toward him as before.

Victoria sometimes came to us with an oilcloth scroll under her arm, marked with a chessboard, and a box of rattling chess figures in her purse, and played chess with either my father or me. She was in her first bloom and I was very young. She emitted a fragrance like that of a rose which stands in the sun and does not really know if it ought to open or not. For the first time I became aware of the curves of a breast, the soft fullness of slender hips. I looked at her from the side, absorbed as if I were intoxicated. She suspected nothing and calmly moved her chess figures on the shining oilcloth. She always wanted to win. We were poor players; she could occasionally have granted us a checkmate.

The time came when I had to decide if I wanted to attend the *Realgymnasium* or the classical *Gymnasium*. I was an average student. Why deny it? The professors therefore did not advise the much more difficult and longer course of the *Gymnasium,* where one had to study Greek, which proclaimed its difficulty immediately with its strange alphabet. But the *Gymnasium* was the prerequisite for the university, for the profession of doctor. I therefore asked my father to permit me to undertake it. He had changed in recent years. Our household cost more money, he had to work more; in fact, he often brought work home. He had to concentrate on his sketches and diagrams. I watched with fascination how he opened the little square bottle with the fragrant black India ink and took the drawing instruments out of their leather case. My mother watched both of us from her chaise longue. About that time she often reminded us that she had made the great sacrifice for us of not going to the sanatorium because she had not wanted to leave us alone. She probably suffered a kind of jealousy and did not like

Victoria's visits. Once she fired a good-looking, industrious, capable maid, Vroni from the Allgau, without giving any reason, and she had been angry with my father for several weeks because he had inquired about the cause for this abrupt action. It was probably her sickness which made her so suspicious.

My father listened absentmindedly to my request to be allowed to attend the *Gymnasium*, filling his drawing pen with India ink and polishing the outside of the delicate instrument with a piece of blotting paper. He did not say so, but he was not especially happy about my desires. Perhaps he thought that I wanted to achieve more than he had. "As a simple government engineer in Upper Bavaria, I have been happy without Greek, but do what you want to."

I was very happy about this answer and moved quickly to his side. I wanted to throw my arms around him. Just because he had seemed somewhat estranged over the previous months, I wanted to thank him especially for his approval. He accepted my embrace but spread both hands over his drawing. It was too late. I had seen that the drawing, done largely in pencil, was no bridge project but a house of several stories in ground plan and elevation. My mother noticed my confusion, which I had not been quick enough to hide. Several days later she asked me about it. I said that I did not know what she was talking about. I never could lie well. If only I had kept still! My foolish comment made her more suspicious. If I had had the courage to tell the truth, maybe I would have prevented much disaster.

But I really wanted only the best. Excitement for my poor mother who was very weak was now "pure poison," as the Kaiser-Jew put it in a banal fashion. "All crying is forbidden!" he commanded her, assuming a free and easy military tone when she began to cry because she had to undergo a small pleural tap. How her tears cut me to the heart! I cannot describe how crushed I was. And I had to assume a bored manner and strive not to let her see my true feelings. If only my poor mother (for the second time in a few lines I call her poor) had suffered from another disease! But pain in the lungs, in the pleura, I knew only too well from my own experience.

The day the tap was to be done, I wanted to leave our house early. The doctor had suggested that she come to his office in a carriage. He would do the tap while she was anesthetized and then, wrapped in blankets, she would be brought home. "No," she said, "a thousand horses could not move me from the spot." "Two would be sufficient," he said sarcastically, but she clung to her home, to me. What could I do? I remained. What I had dreaded occurred, for my presence did not relieve my mother of any pain. I heard her whimpering in the next room. She called for me, but I did not dare to go. The doctor, who in spite of his skill and integrity was at this time a monster — at least he seemed so to me — told her that she should remember that I had endured this little operation with stoic calm and she should not have a "tizzy"! My mother, who was breathing in short, gasping pants, did not answer at first. After a few minutes the doctor asked if she did not feel somewhat relieved. He had removed, as I later learned, some pus from the chest cavity; it was a very successful tap, just as mine had been years before. But my mother was not grateful — or at least she did not want to show it. With some animosity she asked the doctor first, if he always had to use colloquialisms like "tizzy," and second, if he did not fear that he would make me too proud when he held me up as an example to a mature woman, sick unto death, and I was only a "snotty youth"?

He did not give her an answer, tactful for once, and she did not give him a fee. I saw as I entered the room that he was waiting for it; his income could not have been great since he treated many poor people for free — I remembered his joy in the twenty-mark piece that my mother had once given him. But there was nothing to be done. He took his leave, she lay down on the chaise longue with a long, deep sigh that evidently helped her. I stayed with her. I held her thin hands and said nothing. Even I breathed more easily, especially when I saw after an hour the noticeable decrease in her temperature which we had not been able to achieve before, even with compresses. Both my mother and the doctor had been adamant against using medication to reduce the fever.

My father came home somewhat later than usual that day, his face beaming even before he learned of the success of the "little operation." He took a small case of red Morocco leather out of his breast pocket and handed it to my mother. It was a small brooch with a rather expensive stone, an emerald. I do not know how my mother came to the idea that this gift was the sign of a disturbed conscience. In spite of the injunction of "No crying," she began to cry. We comforted her. The decrease in the fever was the best sign — that evening for the first time it was below 38 degrees Centigrade — so why should my father and I have a troubled conscience when we were so full of sympathy? But she resented our sympathy, saying, "Comfort yourselves. I will soon give you your freedom and sink quietly into the grave." She spoke almost inaudibly, as if she wanted to stop herself but could not entirely suppress her true feeling. "Then you can marry again, better than the first time, and can fill the nursery in your villa with babies. And you" — she went on, addressing me — "can write your secrets in ordinary letters."

It may be that many intelligent patients who are bedfast for a long time and can do nothing develop an inordinate curiosity after a time. She had not rested nor stopped looking until she had uncovered my father's drawing. There were in it, to be sure, two rooms facing east which were marked as children's rooms. The poor woman assumed that my father planned a second marriage as soon as she was dead and counted on having more children. After all, a construction engineer can make such a wishful drawing with scrolls and balconies on the façade, pointed roofs, broad halls — simply as an exercise for fun. The drawing was not of recent date. What shocked me was that she had kept her secret so long, that she therefore knew more than we had assumed.

My own conscience was not entirely clear. For a long time I had wanted to draft small sketches for myself, in order to be alone in spirit. My secrets satisfied my need to feel superior to others. I did not like it that my mother ferreted them all out. Those were the years of development — religious doubts and the temptations of my age occupied my attention. My diary helped me very much, for writing it made me see myself. As far as possible I adhered to the truth, and as I reported I judged myself. When I noticed that Mother knew of these things — she could not keep entirely silent, just as she had brought the matter of the nursery to light — I began to write the sketches, which were as a rule quite short, in Greek. (I was learning Greek at the time.)

I must say that one can love another person from the depths of one's heart and think of him as part of one's self, and at the same time have a desire to keep some things secret from him.

This outburst had no good results. It did not help my mother's health. The doctor was right: crying was forbidden. My father continued with his plans — perhaps he was even more determined than before. I did not write any more diaries, but each day I set aside a little piece of wood — sometimes a board, sometimes a branch — with some symbols scratched on them which reminded me of something special and which I kept in an unused washstand. No one else could decipher them; in fact, after a time I could do it only with great difficulty.

Some improvement in my mother's condition became noticeable; it was very slow and amounted only to the fact that she suffered no relapse and that the dreaded tap did not have to be repeated. When I was in the last year of the *Gymnasium* and was preparing myself for the *abitur,* my mother finally decided to go to the sanatorium. The expenses were not minimal; she asked my father about it rather fearfully. He, however, agreed almost before she had finished asking. He said that he would provide everything that an ordinary civil servant could for his beloved little wife. My mother prepared for her departure, leaving us in the care of an ugly, lazy cook. When the train had gone, my father offered me a good cigarette from an elegant case which I had never seen before; it was heavy, made of blue-gray Russian silver.

After Helmut had introduced me to the art of smoking during the preceding summer, I had become addicted to it. Actually, he had merely shown me the proper procedure. I had begun to smoke secretly a long time before, but I had not realized that one should inhale the smoke. I had merely blown my breath through the cigarette so that it burned very well, and in the darkness it crackled and sparkled beautifully — but it caused me no problems. When I later discovered how it should be done, it took a long time until I achieved the same pleasure as I had had in the earlier days when I thought that I was smoking.

The reports from the sanatorium were favorable. If I got home first, I opened her letters. My father did the same. He said that he was very busy at the time, although he never brought any work home. He stayed away until late in the night and finally all night. He no longer appeared regularly at noon for dinner, so that my mother's letters began to pile up on the table beside his empty plate.

One clear, sultry May evening, when I had finished my work earlier than expected, I went past my old school in the Meadow Park. There had been much building in the neighborhood in recent years. No horses were to be seen; the cavalry barracks had been moved to a distant suburb, and engineers were in the old barracks. I went rather thoughtlessly through the park, savoring the fragrance of the blooming black alder trees. Ahead of me on a rather shady, steep walk lined with chestnut trees, I saw a couple with a pram. The woman pushed it with her right hand; with her left she walked arm in arm with a man who from behind looked like my father. Since I had no idea that it could be he, I hurried after them. I was horribly taken aback when I recognized the man as my father and the woman with the blue ostrich-feather hat and white gloves on her fat hands as our former maid Vroni.

I stared as if I had been struck by lightning; the monster, grinding, crushing, consuming, which I had not experienced in a long time, overwhelmed me. They, too, were so astonished that they stopped. The pram with its two sleeping children of the same age rolled on for a way because Vroni had let go and the path was somewhat steep. It was I who stopped it. In order to hide my confusion I bent over the carriage, out of which a sweet fragrance arose such as healthy babies have. I could not tear my eyes away. The features of my father were undeniably there.

My father stepped forward and took the wagon back to Vroni. It was a new wagon with good springs. Then he looked at me searchingly and was pleased by what he saw. Instead of hating him and this disloyal maid, instead of feeling that these two illegitimate children were a disgrace, instead of suffering from the injustice which lay in this deception of my invalid mother, I did not hate, I felt no shame, and I did not suffer. And yet I am sure that the idea of the sanatorium had only seemed to be my mother's. In reality, he had let the poor woman ask him for something which was to his advantage and let her even thank him for it.

Instead of all these oppressive thoughts, I experienced such a bright joy, full of grace, as never before. I had not felt like this for a long time. My father understood me at once. He first patted the child lying on the left, whose rich, ash-blond curls fell over its forehead, and pointed to the narrow gold necklace; her name was Finchen. The other child, a duplicate of the first one, whose hair was under a light blue velvet cap, was Max. These were my brother and sister. I had a brother and a sister, something which I had always wanted. I was the oldest of us three.

My father relaxed then — at least it seemed so to me. Vroni remained embarrassed; she did not know how to address me, and she tried to speak in High German. I told her to call me by my first name. They did not want me to leave. Instead of returning to our lonely apartment, I had to go with them to their home, which pleased me greatly. It was furnished with the most modern and beautiful furniture, which he himself had created. The children's room in light yellow and light blue was charming. I could hardly tear myself away, but I finally went home. He stayed with them. I was so tired that I deciphered the most recent letter of my mother only with effort. She too was happy. She was better.

The *abitur* examinations were scheduled particularly early that year; I passed mine at the end of June. I wanted to tell my mother of this happy event immediately in a letter that my father and I would write jointly. He convinced me, however, not to mail this letter and to let my mother think that the examination was much later. Then she would come later from the sanatorium, which would be to her advantage, and we would meet in S. for the vacation. I agreed. Although this was a silent deception, I had no qualms of conscience about it.

My father was happy; he was successful in everything. It pleased me to be able to help him in the continuance of his pleasant life.

I made a second mistake, perhaps somewhat more pardonable. Years earlier, my mother had given me on my saint's day a pair of silver candleholders so that I could have light if I wanted to read during the night. Shortly afterward electricity was introduced, and I did not need the candelabra. I had stored them in the unused washstand which was closed with a movable board and in which my diary on bits of wood was kept. Now I got the idea that I ought to give the twins a present. The candelabra were of less use to them than to me, but they were nice, heavy pieces. In any case, I would make my father happy. I wrapped the things in tissue paper, tied the package with a little gold cord, and took it to them. He was immoderately pleased, told Vroni to bring candles, and in the evening we sat quietly by candlelight at the bed of the twins, smoking cautiously so as not to provoke them to coughing. Vroni had nursed them beforehand and smiled proudly and yet shyly as she looked at all four of us.

Several days later my father came for me at our house and took me in a magnificent, rented four-seater car, which was waiting in the street, to a prestigious suburb located on a hill, where large splendid villas such as he had once sketched were situated in wide, deep, parklike grounds. His was now being built. He had obtained the land through the friendship of one of his superiors in the office. On this occasion I began to be disturbed for the first time. For whom was he building? The villa was much too big for us; my mother, who preferred a small, quiet household, would not be comfortable there. He certainly could not occupy the villa with his second family. He could not even give it to them; that would be too obvious. Or was he assuming that death would release him from my mother? I could not believe him to be so inhuman. And he was not. At that time he just did not think anymore. He reasoned just as little as I did, even though I knew that my mother with her over-developed curiosity would sniff out my diploma and uncover the exact date of my *abitur* and that she would sooner or later inquire about the candleholders. But I acted as I was irresistibly driven to by my heart and soul. I was so starved for cheerfulness, for health, for enthusiasm, for courage, for a worry-free life, that contrary to my nature I buried all my scruples and lived day by day as he did. The truth at that point would have been for both of us sobering and gray; a short time afterward it became very bitter, and its consequences determined the course of the rest of my youth.

My father went to an official test of a bridge for a few days and Vroni went to her parents' home in the Allgau with my brother and sister. I read in the paper, on the fourth page and in small type, that an accident had occurred in the locality where my father was. A railroad bridge had collapsed, fortunately with no fatalities, but of those working on the structure one had been seriously injured and four or five slightly. The monster, grinding, crushing, consuming, engulfed me again.

I imagined my father lying on his face amid the wreckage, badly wounded, groaning because of severe pains, his chest crushed by square stones and beams, and I had to convince myself forcibly that as chief engineer he was not included among those "working on the bridge." I hurried to the post office, telegraphed, and in two hours had an answer that nothing had happened to him and that I should meet him at the station. He came, looking very pale, saying nothing, and warding off my embrace. He telephoned his Vroni from the station post office. Obviously he wanted reassurance. I stormed him with questions. He became gloomy but controlled himself, assumed his modest smile, and put me off to the next day. The next day my mother arrived. He knew how to arrange matters so that she heard nothing, at least not from him or from me, since he had obtained my word of honor to remain silent.

Soon, however, we learned the entire truth through the newspaper. The bridge, like all official structures, had to be accepted by a commission. Two railroad trains, their cars loaded with stones, were used in the test. This time, unfortunately, one arch was not strong enough. Carelessness and personal fault? But it could also have been a failure in the material or the fault of a contractor.

As the engineeer in charge, my father was immediately suspended from his post; a careful investigation began. At home he acted as if nothing had happened. Soon, however, we hardly saw him; he left very early in the morning and came home late in the evening. He was very subdued, but he could barely maintain his self-control. I did not dare open the newspaper for fear of learning something horrible. But we were spared nothing. My father's papers at the office had been investigated, the bills and vouchers checked, and from these it became clear that his immediate superior and he had received significant sums from one of the supply companies. The material ordered from them was of poorer quality; the traverses had been too weak.

There was a legal suit, the complaint spoke of negligence, physical injury, passive and active bribery — passive because they themselves had taken money, active because they had directed a small portion of the bribes to others in the lower ranks, including the overseer in whose area the accident had occurred. It was fortunate that the accident had been no worse; a much worse one could have happened if the test had not been so carefully carried out — for example, if the bridge had collapsed under the weight of a passenger train.

During this period I saw that my mother had become composed, imperturbable. She wanted to keep us so far as possible out of the scandal of the trial, which she considered lost even before it began. Correctly, too. She wrote to her uncle, asking if he could not keep us for the immediate future. He took his time in answering, but finally a favorable response did come. We packed in a hurry, but before we left, the rest of the disaster broke over Mother and me. Fortunately her health was good now so that she could bear everything. She had gained weight, her eyes seemed much smaller now between her leathery, firm, smooth cheeks, browned by the sun, and it seemed to me that she had fewer gray hairs than before.

I had thought that the worst was over, but I was wrong. I did not see what I should have seen if I had used my reason.

My father had delicately implied to me once that his Vroni had been much sought after. Among her other suitors was his superior in the office, the director, who had helped him acquire the villa. He had courted her again and again but had always encountered an ice-cold refusal. I could not really understand that. For Vroni had not appeared to me as especially desirable. Her first youthful bloom had faded; she tried, often unsuccessfully, to assume "noble" manners, to eat with tensed fingers and to talk in a "refined" manner. Perhaps I came to this denigration of Vroni because I had often battled and won over my own temptations by considering women of easy approach nothing more than "impure vessels" and had held myself as aloof from them as possible because I considered myself too good for them.

But this report of my father's must have had a basis in fact. The wife of the director had heard about it, and it was the natural jealousy of such an "impure vessel" to seek revenge and to find the surest way of avenging her injured feminine pride on her rival.

Something else entered here, too. My father had been allowed to go free. Obviously his fault was not as great as that of his superior. Later, it is true, the suspicion was expressed, again by the director's wife, that my father had blamed his superior too strongly in order to clear himself. The outcome of the trial seemed to indicate that. Nonetheless, I have always found it difficult to believe this.

Circumstances developed with great speed, one after the other.

35

First, without explaining anything to me, my mother gave up her plan to travel to my uncle and to leave my father alone. Finally one evening about a week before the trial, my mother came to the table with a haggard face, but she said nothing to me or to my father, who was sitting withdrawn, emaciated and pale in the corner of the room. She set the two blasted candleholders with a crash on the table — without candles, of course, for it was still light.

Then we learned (my mother could not keep it secret) that the director's wife had invited my mother to her home for a "comfortable" chat. She told my mother that it was not my father but rather her own husband who had seduced the pretty maid Vroni. But he had soon tired of her and had permitted my father to succeed him. Vroni had been quite unwilling but had yielded after my father had given her magnificent presents and had promised to have a two-story villa built for her on the Herzog hill. She bore him the two children; he had been so ecstatic in his paternal good fortune that he had promised to marry her. He had told her laughingly that my mother would never come home again, that she was on her last lap. I too had been part of the plot, and had sought to win Vroni for myself by giving her the candelabra, without thinking about incest, just as if I were a Jew. The two women, arm in arm, had gone quietly to Vroni's apartment, had ordered her to vacate the dwelling by the first of the month together with her bastards. They also told her that it would be best if she left the city, boarded out the children, went back into service, and prepared herself to work respectably. They had taken the two candelabra, and the disgraceful woman, while she wept, had tried to kiss their hands, which of course they did not allow.

The candlesticks stood there; there was nothing that I could say. What incest meant, I did not know. Certainly it had something to do with the "impure vessel."

The construction of the villa on the hill was halted; the land was offered for sale. In the course of time it was sold at no loss, perhaps even at a little profit. I did not hear about that until later. But even if I had known about it earlier, it would have changed nothing in my decision or in the course of my life. Vroni's apartment, to which she had no legal claim, was sold to the highest bidder; it brought in very little, for the beautiful furniture designed by my father was considered too modern. Our own furniture went the same way, only somewhat later. It produced more since it was in an old-fashioned style. All that is secondary. The chief thing is that my father was declared innocent of crime for lack of evidence but was declared liable under civil law. I myself always considered this a contradiction — he was either guilty or not.

My mother, after the acquittal, attempted to question me: "How could you tolerate such a thing? How could you be so two-faced? Don't you love me?" I loved her more than ever. But what had happened, had happened. If only I could have lied! If only I could have been deceitful! Or could have shrugged it off!

Soon my father succeeded without difficulty in reconciling himself with her, to be sure, in a way that kept me at a distance for a long time. Perhaps wrongly. Perhaps he acted in self-defense. Misfortune makes people vulgar. Gratitude leads to meanness.

The fact was that all the world avoided us as if we had the plague, the Kaiser-Jew and his daughter were the only ones who remained loyal. We were not repulsive to them; they helped us. There was hardly any money available; my mother told me that without looking at me. Her uncle, who had learned everything from the newspapers, did not answer. My father's salary had stopped. The civil suit with its promise of misfortune was before us. The doctor, who lived in very modest circumstances, lent us what he could spare. His daughter took care of our household for a few days since even the old, lazy, ugly cook had turned her back on such a shameless house. My father did not deal with facts but with prejudices. He lied steadfastly because he hoped that the lie would be accepted by my mother, because it opened the path to reconciliation. He blamed the Kaiser-Jew; he had advised my father, an honest Bavarian, by pettifoggery and according to the Talmud to establish a healthy, well-born family. The doctor was supposed to have said that my father must know that all was lost in the case of my mother, that the sickness had made her intolerable, and that my father should consider it fortunate that he was losing an evil, quarrelsome wife and gaining a thoroughly healthy woman, suited to motherhood, like Vroni. Not a word of it was true, but my father figured as did many others later — and like them he met with success. My mother believed him. She forgave her husband. She dropped me. Wringing her hands, she said, still not looking me in the eye, that I was worse than a Jew, that I was a Judas who had betrayed her, my father and myself — and without payment, simply out of a desire for treachery in order to know what it was like. And after all this I was no longer her child.

I was silent and ashamed. I reminded myself how disillusioned my mother must be; she had returned home from her suffering a restored, happy woman — to find everything in collapse. I loved her. I felt with her much more than with myself. I would not have betrayed her, but rather myself.

I preached patience to myself. I was young, I could wait. Time was on my side; it would heal everything. Whether or not I was still her son in her eyes was unimportant. I still stayed with her, we continued to live under the same roof, and we would find each other again, I thought. But it never came to that. I do not know if that was fortunate for me or not.

My father overcame his humiliation more easily than I had thought possible. In a short time he found new acquaintances (they could not be called friends). Besides, he thought seriously of settling permanently in S. and believed that the news of his trial and his Vroni would not reach there or that the natives were more practical about such things.

More important was what he called his modest financial position. This was now more than modest. He had put all of his sizable savings and a part of the not insignificant dowry of my mother into the new building. (My parents, however, told everyone very plainly that they had nothing left.) He had deposited notes with a real estate broker, and viewed it as good fortune that he was allowed time to pay until the valuable property on the Herzog hill was sold. He had no income. He did have debts, especially to Dr. Kaiser. He wrote him an ice-cold, formal letter which ended with the words (I read them with shame and sorrow) that he hoped that he would not find the doctor a second Shylock, a foreigner, who with a note in his hand would cut out the flesh from the body of a well-intentioned native. The doctor, knowledgeable about people, from whom the aphorism came that gratitude commits one to meanness, comforted himself more easily about the loss of the money than about the loss of our family. He was accustomed to us. He would have been glad to have me visit even after all these circumstances. But that could not be; I did not want to straddle the fence anymore, and he understood. In fact, he was so tactful that he did not tell his daughter about his being repulsed, maybe because he was an incorrigible optimist; and so Victoria, suspecting nothing, came to see us one day. My mother sent her away with scornful words spoken through a crack in the door, without letting her enter. I saw her leaving, blushing with shame but not downtrodden, rather with a masterful, angry expression. There, too, I hoped that time would correct everything and that my mother would sometime see her wrong and repent.

My father, whose guilt was accepted by everyone who had any feeling for right and wrong, even though he was not punished, worked himself out of his difficulties by saying that all of us are human. When he was required to pay a pension to the badly injured worker, he complained about the money of the proletarians, which they earned so easily. And four grown, cunning people — my parents, the director's wife and their lawyer — "paid" the pale, poorly dressed Italian, who barely spoke German and who carried his arm, broken at the shoulder, in a dirty sling, a pittance in exchange for the pension in future years. But in the meantime even this pittance had to be paid. My mother sold some jewelry and cried bitterly. She was allowed to cry now. I thought of the days before we made the pilgrimage to Altötting, when we had stood in front of the jeweler's window, and again how years later, after her "little operation," my father had brought her the piece of jewelry with the emerald. She refused to give that up; it was too precious in her memory.

In the meantime a development occurred which seemed to indicate that fate was about to help me. My uncle, to whom I had written on the insistence of my parents, using the best penmanship I could, answered me personally with even fancier, though almost illegible, writing. He offered me a stipend, to be paid until I finished the university, when I would be certified as a doctor. It was sufficient — a hundred marks a month.

This sum was especially welcome to me. A few weeks earlier I had suggested to my parents that I would stay through the summer until late fall in our apartment, take care of it, cook my meals, and so forth; they could then rent my room in S. to a stranger. Now there was some money. I told my parents that I would give them seventy-five marks a month. The first installment had arrived at the same time as the letter to the address of my mother. I assumed that they would take me along to S. and not rent my room, and that I would be paying the seventy-five marks only until fall. My parents, one heart and soul now as never before (it may be that I was for the first time somewhat jealous of my father), took these contributions for granted. But they did not let me go along, and they never thought of giving up the money, which was always sent to their address. They were in need, and they thought first of themselves; after all, they were no longer young. Perhaps they believed that my uncle, who had answered my first letter so generously, would be more generous toward a second begging letter — and money was money, wherever it came from.

So I had only twenty-five marks a month. But I lost even those through my own behavior — I had not learned my lesson — because of my own foolishness, because of my own high spirits, because of the desire to play God, because of my illusions of grandeur. My mother had been very right when she once upon a time told the Kaiser-Jew that he should not foster my illusions. Was an eighteen-year-old, inexperienced, dependent solely on himself — for I could no longer accept anything from the goodhearted poor Kaiser-Jew, not even advice — was such a person, who knew the hardships of life only from hearsay, not suffering from illusions when he had the feeling that three people were being grossly mistreated, Vroni and his brother and sister, and therefore sent them the rest of the money because his father, who was morally responsible for these three people, modestly withdrew his support under the guise of civil law, which turns an unmarried mother into the street, assuring her of the customary alimony? Had I not seen in the case of the Italian what legal rights in the hands of the proletariat mean? With the pitiable alimony, the two children and Vroni could live only in the greatest want; she told me of that in a message written in the margins of an old newspaper with a dull pencil while the twins wailed in chorus, no longer so blooming and beautiful as a few weeks before. If she had nothing more than the alimony, she would have to give the children up and go into service. So I added twenty marks a month. Vroni certainly never believed that they came from me, who was now beggared. She thought that my father was a noble gentleman, and that he had the money sent to her in this way so that she would not thank him and so that his wife knew nothing of it and could not object. Vroni was not equal to writing and reading, but she could calculate, and she was very clear about his and our circumstances.

PART II

I, TOO, GRADUALLY LEARNED to calculate because I had to. I learned to figure in terms of loneliness, and money, and poverty. Up to now I had always been with my parents and had lived without a care. Now I got up in the morning and said good-morning to no one; in the evening I went to bed and said good-night to no one.

It rained a lot at that time. I thought of my parents in their little cottage in S. — how the rain added to their problems, how it would make it more difficult to rent the extra room to a tourist. I could not break my ties to them, neither by day nor by night. When I woke up in the night because of some kind of horrible dream, in which either the ungrateful horse or the moor played a role, I listened to the adjacent room for either the light cough of my mother or the heavy breathing of my father, forgetting momentarily my situation. I was their child, whether they wanted it so or not. The electricity had been cut off, but the two beautiful, heavy candlesticks were still there. In the pantry I found several ends of candles, together with some dried-up onions and a thick bunch of old keys, so I began to write; I had an urgency to write them, I who had always been silent. The next day I bought a whole pound of good wax candles. The postage for the heavy letter was ten pfennigs. There were all kinds of expenses at once. I thought that my parents would ask me to come, that they could not manage without me regardless of what they had decided. Therefore I would take the letter with me and save the money. Besides, I could sleep overnight in S. for ten pfennigs — in fact, for five pfennigs at the lake inn, or for free in the haymow of a farmer. But no letter came from my parents. I was too proud to beg. Slowly I grew accustomed to being alone. It was hard, but —!

To get along on my money proved likewise to be difficult. My mother had often complained how impossibly expensive living had become; I had not believed her. Now I discovered it for myself. At first, because I felt I had to be among people, I had permitted myself the luxury of going to a tavern. I have never been a drinker;

I left my mug untouched. I just did not want to be alone. Although such a mug cost only thirteen pfennigs, with the tip fifteen, and although I saved as much as I could in buying my food, bread and bacon, my money diminished rapidly.

I could have started walking to S., but I did not want to be a burden to anyone. After I had so generously disposed of my stipend to my legitimate and illegitimate family, I really could not arrive on foot like a wandering hobo. But there certainly was not enough money left for train fare, as I discovered by checking the fares at the station.

I had another idea. I still had the two heavy candlesticks. There was nothing to stop me from pawning them. That certainly was neither giving them away nor selling them. It only meant that I was entrusting them to the Royal Bavarian pawnshop for a time. So I walked quietly there, stood a long time in the poor air among miserable creatures who carried either their bedding or Sunday clothes, which smelled musty, or clocks or jewelry. I finally received not a penny more than three marks for the two beautiful candelabra. At first I was tempted to refuse the money. But the official showed me apathetically that they had only a thin outer shell, a veneer, of silver and that the weight came from lead, out of which they had been poured. So I sauntered off and heard as I was leaving that the people behind me, who had pawned a heavy featherbed, were likewise unhappy. Had the featherbed also been poured out of lead? No, but it had not been disinfected.

I had assumed that I would get at least fifteen marks for the holders, but I was not discouraged. The first joys of freedom began to develop again. A great ease in life, coming and going as I wanted to, to live and let live, to bear the few unavoidable hardships with stoic dignity, to let God be a good man, to be stubborn and healthy with the future ahead — all this made me happy in spite of difficulties.

I went through a misty rain to the main station. There the sturdy porters dressed in wide blue-and-white-striped smocks, most with mustaches and red cheeks, had their place under the smoke-blackened arcades. With a cigar or a pipe in their mouths they waited for travelers, who because of the rotten weather were few and far between. The work area for these official porters was the station. Beyond it they carried luggage for no one. They made no "commissions." They did not recommend strangers to inexpensive quarters, and so on.

This was done by all kinds of dubious people without official position, without numbered badges, and without blue and white smocks. One of these unattached porters approached me, fooled by my good suit, and offered to obtain for me a nice lodging at the East Gate for a mark a night. He was a rather emaciated, pale, ungainly young man who smelled strongly of gentian brandy. I told him that he should not make a fool of himself, that I was no stranger, that he was more of a stranger than I. This was actually the case; he had walked from Alsace and wanted to go to Budapest, but had not yet gone on his way. We started talking, and I paid for a liter of beer for him in the station restaurant, third class – or rather I paid for two, for he drank mine as well. When he looked longingly at the bottle of gentian brandy on the buffet I treated him to that, too, resolving that this would have to be my only dissipation for a long time. He gulped the brandy down in one swallow and coughed horribly. He did not thank me very cordially and returned to the arrival hall; he looked exhausted, and his face was even paler than before.

He was approached by a small caravan of strangers with a great many packages as well as a huge trunk, which two of them carried awkwardly between them. He was to bring the trunk and direct them to a very cheap lodging. He could manage the latter easily, for he had more than fifty good addresses listed on the last page of a well-thumbed paperback. But bringing the trunk was something else – he was too weak, almost like paper which a wind could blow away.

I put the trunk without effort on my shoulders, and so we marched through the wet streets to a rather miserable section of town which I had almost never visited, even though it was not far from our home. Carrying the trunk on the street was nothing, but getting it up the narrow, winding staircase was something else. That trick had to be learned. I bumped into the walls at least twenty times, and my old chest wound began to pain me. But upstairs, as I wiped the sweat from my forehead with my right hand, I received in my left a new silver mark, the first money that I had ever earned. The good-natured wife gave me in addition a tarnished, thin silver fifty-pfennig coin.

I did not have the heart to let our guide go empty-handed, since the strangers assumed that he would be paid by the landlord, who assumed that he was paid by the tourists! I therefore gave him the fifty pfennigs, with which he could buy himself four liters of beer with as much bread as he wished, or one liter with a nice sausage, or a very small glass of sharp brandy.

I saw him often after that.

One day he offered me for two marks his rust-red little book of La Rochefoucauld with all the valuable addresses. I had just sold my beautiful stamp collection for thirty-two marks. I had spent most of my allowance throughout my youth for rare, usually genuine, valuable stamps, and I thought of Helmut, who had given me the idea, and also a little about his father, whom I compared with mine.

Because the two marks seemed expendable, I was ready to do business. At home, by the light of a candle without a holder, I looked through the booklet and found all kinds of truths, mostly bitter, which I did not really understand, but there were no addresses. I did not need them; for my porter-brother they were daily bread or daily gentian brandy. He had secured them from another porter, who in the meantime had moved on to Italy.

At first I leafed so aimlessly among the maxims of the old stoic and incorruptible Frenchman that I thought the translation must be in error. Suddenly the thought occurred to me to use my unlimited free time to learn French by means of La Rochefoucauld. I went to the large city library with trepidation and obtained a French book and a French-German dictionary; with these I attempted to translate. Since the varying forms of the verbs were unknown to me, I had to trouble the librarian again for a grammar. When I finally translated a short maxim I was filled with great pride. I asked myself why I needed to spend my whole life in Germany. I wanted to learn French, then English and also Italian — all while I was studying medicine, which I was anticipating eagerly. As a full-fledged doctor I wanted to travel throughout the world: Europe, Africa, Asia — I wanted to be at home and to earn my bread by means of my professional skills in any and every corner of the earth. It was the ideal of cosmopolitanism which appeared so beautiful to me.

In the meantime the fall was passing quickly; the evenings were long. I inquired at the university office about the necessary formalities. They were explained to me by an officer of one of the leading fraternities, who had stationed himself there in order to gain freshman members. He gave me all the information I wanted and added that his "brothers" would be pleased if I were to join them sometime in X tavern. I answered evasively; I knew positively that I would never join a fraternity. I did not like to be jammed up with a lot of people in one room; I hated every restriction; I could not tolerate drinking beer; and first and foremost I had no money.

I had discovered that the fees for the first semester amounted to one hundred and ten marks, and I expected to receive this money from my parents. I knew that my mother had kept a small reserve, a savings account, and I also knew that for three months I had been giving them seventy-five marks a month. Obviously I had no claim to these anymore. But I did think that my mother could give me an advance of one hundred ten marks, and I would pay this off slowly in the course of the semester.

In the meantime I had learned to calculate better, and had seen that if I lived skimpily I could get along on an income of fifty marks a month. I figured ten marks for shelter, thirty marks for food, and ten marks for incidentals. Besides, I already had five marks, since I remembered that Vroni did not get twenty-five marks a month but only twenty. I wrote this very carefully to my mother. Not to my father. She had made it clear to me before their departure that anyone who wanted anything had to come to her, not to my father, for whatever money she had on hand or received could not be used as indemnity for the damages in the bridge accident.

I wrote again with an embittered heart, sending the letter by registered mail, which cost more, to be sure that it arrived. I waited in vain for word — only the twenty-five marks came with a return address in which my father signed himself as a retired engineering supervisor.

Instead, the workmen came into the house to prepare our apartment for the next tenants; the furniture mover also appeared, to put the furniture in a warehouse until winter, for this was not a good time for auctions. My mother had written *him.*

For several days I was busy from morning till evening with packing furniture and keeping track of rugs, kitchen utensils, dishes, and clothing. I made up a careful list of everything. Then the custodians asked for the keys; there was no rush, they said cordially. I blushed for shame. I had to pack my few possessions; I had to move. I had kept an old but solid trunk, together with some other stuff.

Fortunately I still had twenty marks from the sale of my stamps. I had been living most economically. But no one could give me any clue as to how I could get one hundred ten marks plus fifty marks for the first month of school, how I would manage to exist; no one could suggest a place for me to live. Was I supposed to go on foot to S., which my parents evidently expected me to do? I was strong and healthy; I had grown a good beard, for shaving had long since become too expensive for me. But I did not want to go.

So I began to look for a place to live. I climbed up into all kinds of attic rooms, visited many a little corner without light and filled with the smell of poverty, but everything was too expensive. I told myself that I had to find a place where the rent was absolutely fixed, that is, no more than five marks a month. But the usual little room cost twelve to fourteen marks. Did I have to go to the asylums for the homeless? I did think of it; and in my youthful idealism I did not worry about the vagabonds or even about their lice, for everything was disinfected every night. But how could I work there — and besides, could it be a permanent residence for a student of medicine?

The little porter, addicted to gentian brandy, beaten again and again by life, had an idea. He was adamant about the shelter for the homeless and about several Christian missions which provided shelter but insisted on early rising and prayers. He did have on the sheet torn out of La Rochefoucauld a "very different, high-class" room in the nicest part of town, directly across from the magnificent spire of the cathedral. The address was not cheap; I had to pay him two marks fifty for it, which at that time was a fortune for me. It was an attic room, big enough for a whole family, he told me laughingly. But in order to get to it one had to open an iron door with a key weighing at least a pound, then one had to find his way between the cagelike attic recesses full of dusty trash until one came to a solid door with a padlock. The room had one window, no washstand, no provision for light, no stove, no toilet facilities. There was a large, smoothly planed table, a bedstead with a thin mattress and a coarse sheet. A tin can and a tin washbasin stood on a chair. There were hooks for clothes. There was room enough for trunks and boxes and all kinds of possessions. One did not have to fear thieves.

The swallows, metallic blue-gold, swirled by in the sunset; the bells in the tower rang. I rented it and moved in that same evening.

I had brought with me an old, moth-eaten sheepskin, called a hunting fur. Since there were no pillows on the bed, I put it under my head and slept well. Later it warmed me on cold nights, for the frost came not only through the window but also from the rafters. The water which I used I could pour into the eave troughs rather than carry it back down. The custodian's wife, who rented the room for her own advantage, brought me a lamp, but admonished me to be very careful because of fire. I used it very little, for the lamp consumed oil the way my friend consumed gentian brandy.

Finally a letter came from my parents. My mother asked why I had not come to them. The storage of our possessions and the closing up of our house were long finished. Was I to believe that my mother had kept me in the city for the whole summer after my successful examination only to be watchman and then packer? What was I to do in S.? Should I give up my studies? And what then? Should I be the only one who paid for the embezzlements and love affair of my father? And if she had only asked? But she wrote briefly and curtly, commanding and cold. She demanded the list; I should send it to her. Everything had been packed in boxes except for the hunting fur.

In spite of that I loved the poor woman. I loved her more than ever. I had several pictures of her. I looked at them every day and talked to the pale, old-fashioned portraits as if they were pictures of a saint, of someone who had died. She too thought of me. She reproached me with great bitterness that I associated with worthless tramps in the third-class section of the station, that I drank too much and smoked and injured my health for a lifetime. Was that her reason? I received only twenty-five marks a month from my parents. Even if she assumed that I could eat adequately with that, what was there left for smoking and drinking? At the time they moved, I bought a package of cigarettes every other day, twenty-five for a mark; now a carton with seventy-five cost only fifty pfennigs, and it had to last a week. It was a bitter weed. And I was prepared to give it up too, if it had to be. It was more difficult for me to give up cigarettes than warm food. My parents seemed to have no idea of how I lived — and of course they could not know, for I had kept it from them that I sent Vroni and the twins twenty of those twenty-five marks every month. And they, too, had to live very differently. Could that be called carrying water on both shoulders? But it was my misfortune to understand both sides, to be an eyewitness, not to judge, and not to be a pharisee.

My mother had a long, serious illness behind her. Because of it she had become grasping. My father was no longer what he had been. He had sunk too quickly from the heights of being an engineering supervisor and a builder of villas and the mainstay of two families and of irreproachable reputation — I will not say why. He clung to my mother, both clung to me — to my fixed income, to my future. And I? I wanted to adjust; I wanted to use the relatively large sum from my uncle for myself and my studies, as he had specified. They did not understand this. My father did not approve of too much education; he had shown this earlier in his scorn for Greek. At the same time he had secured his technical training only by means of great sacrifices. My mother too did not appreciate the profession of medicine — even though she owed her little bit of life to the labors of doctors, extending over many years. But did she realize that? She had made a new vow in the sanatorium, and that was supposed to have worked wonders. They wrote me therefore that I should come and help them build a new life. My little room was vacant. A young woman tourist from North Germany had lived in it most recently; she had become dearer to them than a daughter.

I should study — good. They would not renege on their word. But not right now. I should first help my father, and in this way repay him gratefully for my expensive education. They were planning to produce little wooden houses out of weatherproof boards which he called Swedish pavilions. He wanted to begin their manufacture in a small way: the veneer could be sawed and pressed and impregnated in the village. There was a need for these little houses, fabricated one after the other according to a carefully constructed model. Just in S. he could have more than a dozen orders immediately. I would have to stay only until everything ran smoothly. My parents figured that it would take no more than two years — and I would be only twenty then. My uncle did not need to know anything about it. I could bring this sacrifice — deceiving a stranger, as it were, for the sake of my own father — for the seventy-five marks were indispensable, and twenty-five marks really ought to suffice for cigarettes.

I accepted this fact. My decision was made in a moment — to get along without the money but nonetheless to study medicine and not to take away the twenty marks from Vroni. I had shelter. I would earn my food by occasional work: carrying baggage or washing dishes in a hotel kitchen. Vroni had been offered such work, but it was too dirty for her. She was right. But I had no choice. In this way I could earn two or three marks a day. I thought about tutoring but gave up the idea. Manual labor was preferable.

The great obstacle was the hundred and ten marks for the fees. I wandered through the streets all day looking for a solution. Finally a strange idea occurred to me. I found the home of the Fool's Kaiser and asked for Helmut. I knew that he had long ago gone to a military academy in G. When I was told this information, I asked for permission to speak to the councillor. The Fool's Kaiser had just been named an Imperial Bavarian Privy Councillor. The celebration of this honor had come at the same time as his fifth wedding. He had married a new wife a few months earlier who was supposed to be wonderfully beautiful. I had to wait a long time.

The bell rang often, and patients were led into the waiting room. I had not been invited to enter it and waited in a corridor — not in the main hallway but in another which resembled a mountain pass, for on both sides dusty books and unopened brochures and magazines were piled up. I was suddenly so tired that the thought came to me that I should forget everything. Only the waiting had made me tired, not the resistance, not the difficulties.

But finally the councillor came. He knew me from S. He knew at once that I had not come because of Helmut, and he asked me, while he picked a magazine out of the rubbish and dusted it on his white jacket: "What do you want?" I answered him with no formalities: "I need one hundred ten marks." He was surprised that I spoke without embarrassment and without hedging. I did not beg. No one likes to give to a beggar. He continued to look at the pages of the brochure, but insisted by his silence that I continue talking. His firm chin protruded out of his collar as he continued to read. I did not obey. I was silent. What needed to be said had been said. I saw that he was observing me steadily and that he was not interested in the magazine. Finally he capitulated. To be sure, he said nothing, but he dug around in the breast pocket of his smock and pulled out of his thick, disorderly wallet a hundred-mark bill and a twenty-mark. He gave me the money but did not take my hand. "You have to earn the money here in the future, but get a certificate testifying to your destitution so that you can study for free." He remained standing in the corridor while I left the house by the servants' entrance.

I knew through Helmut that his father expended much for people, that is, for beautiful women and also for "scientific co-workers," whom he paid in part as assistants and in part as private secretaries on a temporary basis.

He was a scholar who was possessed by constantly changing ideas, and he was not without success as a theoretical scientist. Whether he had practical results as a doctor, his son did not know. But he commented that that did not minimize the greatness of his father. Actually, Helmut was blinded by his worship of his father in spite of his harsh treatment. His father, he maintained, was a genius, but the mentally ill cannot be saved even by the hand of a genius. They can be studied and observed throughout their lives, and after they die their brains can be viewed under a microscope. But no man had yet appeared who consciously and methodically had given reason back to a mental patient. And after all, the phlegmatic Helmut added, why bother? There had to be fools, if for no other reason than that his father could feel like the Lord God among them.

I had the opportunity myself, years later, to watch Kaiser at the bedside of his patients or in the park. I saw him treat the patients in a paternal, almost comradely fashion as he spoke to them or sought to influence them. Almost all of them, even those only slightly ill, were, if one observed them closely, in another world than Kaiser or I or the attendants, and it seemed to me sometimes that the mental patients and the half-insane influenced the healthy more than vice versa.

He treated them with more consideration than he did his own children. Once in S. he had beaten Helmut unmercifully because of a minor cigarette theft, but he dismissed his top attendant after fifteen years in this responsible position because he had given a violent patient a light blow which the latter had not even noticed. In fact, he had responded to it with peals of laughter.

Sometimes I had the impression that Kaiser revered the mystical darkness of these impenetrable spirits; it attracted him with magical force, and he enjoyed being in the presence of raving, sadness, joy, mystery, confusion, despair, deterioration.

Kaiser treated me sternly and matter-of-factly. If I had thought that the hundred and twenty marks were to be easily earned, to use an expression of my father, I was sadly mistaken.

The academic year began. During the day I was in the lecture rooms, studying anatomy, physiology, botany, mineralogy, chemistry. Afterward I went to the library, for I could not afford to get my own books.

The money I needed to sustain life I earned in the kitchen of a great hotel, the Prince Regent of Bavaria. Carrying bags at the station was no longer profitable in late autumn.

I could help with the dishwashing only in the evening, but they took me on. I soon saw that they had accepted me out of good will. They had recognized that I was an impoverished student from a good family, even though I never said so, and that they did not need to count the silver after I had finished washing it. Real silver was used in the Prince Regent. At first I washed slowly and poorly and broke many dishes in my attempts to work faster and better.

Washing plates is much more difficult than you might imagine. Washing ten plates is no problem. But when you get to the fifteenth or the hundredth plate and still more dishes are brought into the basement by the dumbwaiter, and you take hold of a plate spattered with remnants of fat and food, hold it under the hot water and scour it with a brush, no longer new, which has become soft and is encrusted with repulsive white fat, and when the smell of the fat and of the food and of the lye soap is omnipresent (the smell of game which was especially plentiful at that time was at first particularly odious to me) — then sometimes all your strength deserts you, and a plate falls. But you recognize by the inner jubilation when you hear it clatter and break on the stone floor, and see all the glistening fragments, how repugnant the plates and bowls have become.

But I forced myself with all my strength not to hate the plates anymore, not to detest the smell of fat and of venison, and to do for the little bit of money what was expected of me; for in spite of good will for the needy student, one expected good work — and rightly so.

At first I ate after work in order to be able to enjoy the food in peace. Then I washed my hands with strongly perfumed soap.

Sometimes I could even bathe — but I soon gave up this procedure. My hunger was completely dissipated by the work, and I could not bear the smell of anything cooked or fried, so that I left with an empty stomach. I asked the good-natured supervisor of this part of the hotel management, who had begun as a dishwasher, if I could eat before working, and she granted my request even though the other workers protested, for they hated me as a proud intruder who was too educated. And how hard I had tried to be modest! Not everyone succeeds as well as my father. But we finally made our peace, for we were all in the same boat.

I had considered it only a formality that the councillor had told me to see him again. I was not troubled about the hundred and twenty marks. But it was not meant like that. I telephoned him one evening because I was conscientious. I assumed that I would not be permitted even to speak to him, so I was astonished when I recognized his voice and when he bitterly berated me for having waited so long. I should come to him immediately. Fortunately, it was Monday, my only free evening in the week, so I hurried out to his home. He was not there but had left word that I should wait. The receptionist whispered to me that I was to transcribe records. She was not young anymore but still attractive. He always had to have beauty about him.

I was satisfied. I had had some practice in stenography. My notes, which I had first made in German, then in Greek letters, I now did with stenographic hieroglyphics. This time I was permitted to wait in the resplendent reception room, with its old Dutch paintings. The clock struck nine; he did not come. In the adjoining room I heard his young wife sing a little song with a rosy voice, if I may say so, then she talked on the telephone with a friend for a long time, then she entertained herself with a parrot. Finally all was quiet. The clock struck ten; he did not come.

The receptionist entered and warned me not to leave. He would be furious then; in any case, he was already provoked with me. He had often spoken of me and in S. had held me up to the phlegmatic Helmut as an example of the true modern Spartan. Previously I had been considered a model of heroic, stoic bravery by the Kaiser-Jew, and it had not ended well for me.

But what was there to do? At first I sat down; then I lay down on the sofa, awoke at three o'clock in the morning, took off my shoes and clothes. At seven I dressed again, found the receptionist, and asked her to show me the bathroom, where I could not pass up the opportunity for a bath. I left the house at a quarter to eight to go to my lectures. I had drunk some coffee, I was happy, and I sang. He had not come home. No one knew why. At about five in the morning he had telephoned; I should not be awakened but told to telephone him in the morning without fail.

But all my difficulties, even those involved in providing the services demanded by my benefactor, did not frighten me. The more problems, the more energy, I was young and free, and I enjoyed life.

If I had succeeded in being closer to my mother, I would have been completely happy. What did all the new science really amount to compared to her — the elderly, poor beloved? But she wrote to me in businesslike fashion, matter-of-factly. I wanted to answer her in another vein, out of the depths of my heart, but I forced myself to write to her even more coldly. I did not want to be a burden, and gladly renounced for her sake the seventy-five marks and said I would manage to get along. I did not mention my father purposely. I was angry with him because I could no longer respect him as I had — that is, not as I did when he was still successful. My mother must have understood me in this situation better than I understood myself. She took his part, more so in each successive letter, and I remained a disturber of the peace in spite of my apparently generous behavior.

Apparently? Did I not pay for it unduly? Did I not live all alone in my godforsaken attic room? Did I not look every day at her picture? Did I not show that picture everything that I saw and experienced, since I held it by me at the window so that the eyes of the photograph saw the outside world — the church with its carillon and on the horizon the azure, dreamlike chain of mountains? Did she not accompany me in my spirit, in love, throughout the entire day, through the lecture halls, the library, occasionally to the soup kitchen and six times a week to the scullery of the hotel kitchen of the Prince Regent of Bavaria. Once, shortly before Christmas, the supervisor gave each of us a glass of negus. I pressed the hot glass to my cheek and turned it gently back and forth, and thought of the cheek of my beloved mother pressing against mine.

I did not cry, I did not sigh. Ever since my experience with the ungrateful horse I had lost the gift of tears. But I did long for her. But for her as she had once been, not for her as she lived now. Between the two was a great chasm. But I thought and hoped that someday she would have to love me just because she knew me so well. She would recognize this barrier and leave everything to come to me and live with me alone, leaving my father content with his Swedish pavilions.

There was no point in being sentimental and mourning for that which I could not get again, even with all my energy. Christmas came; I expected her in the city. She waited for me in the country. In vain.

Shortly after the beginning of the new year I came to my first dissection in my practical experiments. I had been warned about the odors. But in my case something remarkable occurred. Everywhere now I smelled nothing but fat and slightly tainted venison. It was so noticeable to me that I thought everyone else smelled it, too. One time in a lecture those sitting next to me moved away. It did not occur to me that a few places had become vacant nearer the lecturer; rather, I assumed they had moved because of me. I spoke to them. They did not take the matter seriously; in fact, they considered it a joke. In spite of this, the idea of my bad smell did not leave me.

In the dissection lab I could not detect any smell of decay. The atmosphere of fat stayed with me, as it did at the barber's or in the waiting room of the councillor. I let it be and began to work on the portion of the cadaver which was identified as mine by a little pasteboard card on the corpse. Five fellow students and I were assigned to a slender, delicate, well-formed body; the face was peaceful, even somewhat roguish. Despite the pallor of the face, in which the lips were differentiated from the surrounding skin only by their wrinkles and their somewhat darker color, I recognized it immediately. It was the face of my brandy-drinking brother. I had a gruesome feeling as I took the pasteboard card with my name on it off his left hand, which had been designated as my dissection experiment. The hand was mine, in the laboratory parlance. Sentimental feelings changed nothing of his fate or of my task. I began working — at first with a heavy heart, then more calmly. I proved to be more skillful than I had thought. The assistant who observed us all was not dissatisfied with my work.

In my search for objective science I had not forgotten my gentian-brandy brother. I knew very well what he had been in his lifetime. In fact, I had his stories as a vagabond fixed in my memory. I saw his penciled notes full of wit and irony before me, in which he had commented about La Rochefoucauld. But after a short time I no longer had this in my view — only the tangible, positive miracle of the human hand.

Whoever has grasped this mechanical miracle may sit in judgment on me. Compared to the hand, the mechanics of an automobile, of a loom, of a locomotive with a hundred horsepower, seem to be the work of a bungler — not to mention a stupid cannon which can do nothing more than destroy people. One has to see with one's own eyes how in the minuscule space between skin and bones the most varying muscles, tensors and flexors, nerves, motor and sensory, veins supplying and purging are arranged, how they cooperate, how they complement each other. I was the last one to get up from my work. I had forgotten everything else — even my mother, even Dr. Kaiser, who was expecting me that evening. I went home as if I were in a trance, sank into a dreamless, blessed sleep, and awakened the next morning reborn, with great joy in life.

In the immediate past I had often taken dictation from Dr. Kaiser. At first he had amused himself by trying to plague me by dictating faster than I could write. He succeeded the first time but not the second. I could do what I wanted to, even though it sometimes took a night with many exercises and very little sleep. Often I was so tired that if he paused very long, I nodded, so that he had to shake me. "Wake up, write," he would whisper. I woke up. I wrote. Sometimes after work he asked me, "Do you need some money?" I always did. The expenses of attending the university were greater than I had anticipated. He was not irritated that my debt to him kept growing; perhaps he had anticipated that. This time he excused my absence because of anatomy. In the future he referred to anatomy again and again. In fact, he tested me with more sternness than justice. I thought that he did it for my sake, that he wanted to lead me like a father.

I thought at that time that my life was difficult, but it was really only externally so. Internally it was easy, for the goal which I had set for myself, the profession of doctor, was not difficult, not distant, unreachable, impersonal; in fact, there was every prospect that I would achieve it. My needs were few. As a doctor or a scholar I could live on a very small income. I wanted to wait as long as possible to choose a wife who had the same interests. I did not think of a very young woman, greedy for life. I did not want an "impure vessel," regardless of how smooth and decorative it was. I thought of a woman somewhat older than I, for whom I would not have to battle, about whom I would have no doubts, who would be loyal to me in difficulties and conflicts. It was only later that I recognized that this ideal picture was none other than that of my mother. But I did not want to be her son, whom she had spoiled at first with overabundant love and had weakened for the struggles of life and then had deserted in favor of her husband. I wanted, rather, to play the role of my father, with whom she went through thick and thin.

One day she visited me, climbing the many steps without becoming breathless. I unlocked the heavy attic door and led her by the hand between the attic nooks into my room. She sat down at the window and looked at the view. She did not say much. She needed to fulfill her maternal duty, I thought to myself. She did not express astonishment about my miserable existence. She thought only of the rebuilding of my father's life. She was perturbed that he, "at his age and after all he had accomplished," had to accept deprivations. She wanted to make me believe that he had been unjustly treated. I had always loved her, but I made no effort to detain her longer when she wanted to leave that afternoon. Why did she take the night train?

My natural father did not deign to visit me.

My spiritual father, Councillor Kaiser, certainly thought about how he could benefit from my help. But he also did many kindnesses for me; he taught me what life and La Rochefoucauld had not been able to teach me: to distrust all people, including myself. But was he himself master of this art always and everywhere, an art with which some are born?

He rendered me, further, another great service, apart from the money. In this time of surfeit in our country, which was suffocating because of its delusions of technological progress, gold, industry, political power, and which in the middle of its own overabundance did not know in which direction to move, he showed me that at least in the area of science there were huge barren stretches, that that there were almost immeasurable white spots on the map of the universe of human knowledge and that there was no end to the work — therefore, also, no room for joy, hope, happiness, if one understands by happiness the illusion that one has a task to fulfill in life which is assigned to him and to no one else.

At first, of course, everything was not so philosophical. I washed dishes evening after evening except on Monday. My hands were slippery from the effect of the black soap softened in the water and the white soda powder. Sometimes, smiling stupidly from weariness, I dragged myself as if I had no knees to the telephone to call him dutifully. There in the hotel I could telephone for nothing and save the ten pfennigs necessary in the public telephone. Perhaps it was not only the stern concept of duty but also the daily need which forced me to the telephone. I realized that I could not continue forever eating so little, living in unheated quarters, and working by the sweat of my brow as a dishwasher. He was my only hope.

If I ever believed, however, that he would spare me on this or that evening because of the late hour, since my call sometimes came after he had gone to bed, I was fooled. He never thought of it. I had to repay the money that he had advanced to me. I said that I would not be available before eleven P.M. "Fine, take a droshky. Have him whip the horses and come." Take a droshky! I who earned fifty pfennigs an hour for dishwashing and was not paid any better for his secretarial duties! So, almost dead from exhaustion, I ran all the way. He came down in a scarlet silk robe and smelled of his wife's perfume — she had a mania for perfume, according to the receptionist. The term "mania" was not unusual in the house of a psychiatrist — on the contrary. He never offered me a cigarette or a glass of water, even though he smoked one cigar after the other and gulped down one French cognac after the other. But nonetheless these hours of dictation were a joy to me, not a burden. I went unwillingly to him, but I did not like to leave.

It was the time when exact science was making unprecedented advances in overenthusiastic projects which were made possible by modern technology, the microscope, experiments in general and the lack of prejudice of the scholars for whom there was no God, no Satan, only science with no preconceived concepts. The chemist wanted to develop a synthetic egg white and thereby solve the social problems in a test tube; the nerve specialist and psychiatrist took for granted that someday they would find the spot in the human brain where the center of faith in God or the concept of the ego lay and where mental illnesses had their anatomical source. Human beings, those who rejoiced in the future as well as those who were doubtful and blasé, took it for granted that they could lift every impenetrable curtain of nature regardless of what experiences previous generations had had.

And it went even further. A man like Gottfried Kaiser assumed that he would be able to heal incurable mental illnesses or the inherited weakness of intelligence, imbecility, by an ingenious combination of modern technology — for example, electricity — with pure scientific knowledge. The magnificent progress which the scientific world had made because of the discovery of radium and of the Hertz electromagnetic waves made everything else appear possible. It seemed as if nothing else were necessary but tremendous energy, absolute objectivity and enough time and money to perform the experiments. We — Kaiser and I — had all this under control. What he did not have, I possessed. He had more money; I had more time. It was my capital.

He never shook hands with me, not when I arrived nor when I left. He had a pathological aversion to having his hands touched. This did not disturb us. In time we became almost friends, certainly good comrades in our work.

In the spring I had to pass several preliminary examinations in order to be able to study under a stipend from the state. Kaiser, who had a huge private fortune in addition to his large income and who paid a large alimony to each of his many ex-wives, could have spared me the ordeal of the examinations, which I feared, by giving me a little money. He did not think of it, and he was basically right, of course. I was astonished when I passed with distinction. I had answered every question immediately, exactly and correctly. I kept my triumph to myself. I recognized that I owed it only to the circumstance that I had concentrated on one thing and that I lived more by will power than by emotion. However, I had not given up my one hobby: I had continued with my French — with very little success, I have to admit. For living languages are poorly learned from dead books, in spite of all determination.

Another good result came from the brilliant examinations. When I had finished the last one, I sighed with relief — and what a miracle! — the smell of fat which had followed me so tenaciously and had troubled me so repulsively had disappeared. It never returned. If ever again it hovered over me like a demonic sacrificial cloud, I was never conscious of it.

I had been looking forward to a quiet summer vacation when Kaiser told me that I should accompany him to S. He would pay me thirty marks a month, that is, he would subtract that sum from my debt of almost three hundred marks, and keep me usefully busy. I agreed, happy at the thought of seeing my parents again and of living with them as in the past, always hoping that they would realize their wrong.

At the station in S. we were welcomed not by my parents but by Kaiser's sons, Karl Otto, the eldest, and Helmut, both of whom had come from North Germany. Helmut was no longer as effeminately pretty as he had been when I had gotten to know him. He seemed changed, subdued, sad and retiring, filled with suppressed passion. He was determined to talk to me. I saw that his father did not like it. I postponed a discussion and asked him where his apathy had stayed. My first walk was to our little cottage.

They were sitting together in the garden. My father had become somewhat old and heavy. He had a few light brown boards and a scratch pad in front of him; he was obviously working on his house models. Later he showed me one in a much smaller design. I also met the summer guest, the blond girl, Heidi; she stood in the kitchen in a scanty, multicolored native costume; she was canning fruit — not the tart wooden apples which my mother had tried to cook years before but raspberries, whose marvelous aroma filled the whole house.

We drank coffee in the garden. I was never alone with my parents. After the coffee Heidi lay down in the hammock. My father pushed her cautiously, pulled on his stump pipe, and occasionally glanced at his scratch pad and at my mother, who was darning his socks. It never occurred to them that I might need shelter and food, that is, my father and his summer butterfly. But I caught a glance from my mother in which there was something of her old love and concern, something of her posture as it had been before her pilgrimage. It welled up in me. But I told myself that it was pointless to disturb the past, even though a good opportunity was at hand.

I got up, shook hands with all three (they formed a pleasant, comfortable family circle), and told them that I would be staying in the village but would probably live and eat with the councillor because he needed me in his work. My mother blushed a deep red as she heard me; my father swung the blond girl more gently and pulled harder on his pipe — then all became peaceful and I left quietly. As I looked back through the laths of the gate and the rusty old gong pealed, I saw that my mother had picked up her sock again. She had not looked after me. I did not sigh or complain. I saw what the situation was. I recalled how a half-year before, in the winter, as I held the hot grog glass to my cheek and imagined that it was she — she had been nearer to me then than now.

The councillor was waiting impatiently for me. He had prepared a beautiful, bright room for me on the ground floor, overlooking the lake. I was to eat with the family. I could use the bathhouse and the different rowboats of the family.

There was no mention of hunting this time. He had brought no hunting dogs with him. He had opened his cages. Evidently the animal experiments had not been a great success — at least he said nothing about them.

I never did get to row, and I went swimming less than once a week. I worked. He was concerned at that time with an entirely new mode of experimentation, that is, a systematic, complete, microscopic investigation of a human brain that had been dissected, into about two thousand sections, I think. The difficult mechanical preparation had been done in the city long before. The sections were packed in numbered wooden chests, one hundred in each. The entire cost of the project was more than five thousand marks.

The human brain was no longer unfamiliar to me. I had viewed sections of the tissue often under a microscope, but never before a cross section through the entire brain, which is extraordinarily difficult to reconstruct, always only in parts. I could differentiate rather easily the outer crust from the deep layers. I knew what a nucleus was, a ganglion, a nerve sheath, a marrow thread, a course, a motor or sensory conductor, but this miserable elementary wisdom was all.

I must thank Kaiser for a seemingly secondary arrangement. In the entire five and a half years I worked for and with him, he meticulously avoided disturbing the sequence of my regular studies. Even though I was curious to study the brain of a paralytic under the microscope, to understand the case history of an insane person, or to investigate such clinically or through psychiatry, he never let me do it ahead of time. I did not learn about mental diseases from him until they were covered in the regular course of study, in the fourth year.

That summer he sat down with me. He showed me many details which would have escaped me or any other uninitiated observer. He never lost his patience. Many times I would rather have dived into the blue-green lake, crystal-clear with waves caused by the east wind. But he kept me at my work. Without words, without promises, matter-of-factly.

He did not manage as well with his young wife, probably because he was not so quiet with her. Katinka, who had looked forward throughout all the months in the city to being together with her husband, knocked on the door. Her rosy voice held a childlike, magical quality. Her little dog whined and barked. He let her wait, then finally asked me to tell the three boys (the youngest had also arrived) that they should take their mother (who was really not related to any of them) for a walk to the Oster Lakes, but to be careful about the treacherous moor.

He rarely spoke of personal matters with me. I had already noticed this in the city. But nonetheless many things became clear to me in time. For I always tried to read other people as I did myself in order to be able to control them as I did myself.

He, with his gray hair and weathered features, loved, this time — as he had always done — passionately, almost unconsciously, like a youth, forgetting everything around him. That is how he began each time. He idolized Katinka, who had the perfume mania, the rosy voice — a fine, aristocratic creature. (All of his wives came from noble though impoverished families.) After a time, however, he began to see the women more clearly; then he withdrew slowly, carefully, but unmistakably from them and turned again, the mature man that he really was, to his scholarly pursuits. Then he looked for the best way to rid himself of them. But this time the end did not seem to be as successful as the beginning had been. Always before, the women had clung more and more to him as he turned from them. This last one, stupid but extremely attractive, with that flutelike, soulless voice that was hard for him to withstand, knew how to escape from Bluebeard. She laughed and played tricks, but remained cool and capricious, adorned herself to her own satisfaction, perfumed herself for her own pleasure and caressed the brown, curly-haired dog as the councillor himself longed to be caressed. After only two weeks he gave me my daily assignment but stayed only an hour or two. Then he would cling to his wife's side. He was jealous of every glance that she gave any other man, whether it was his son Otto or the homely Helmut or the indigent student on vacation. But I did not respond to these glances. For me she was an "impure vessel," all the more impure the rosier, the more kissable, the daintier she was. He thought that he had won her over again by a new passion. Actually, he had become her slave — and he soon recognized it.

Unfortunately my poor Helmut was also enslaved. He confided in me under an oath of silence that he was completely enamored of an older actor who had followed him so long with his love that he had yielded, not aware of what joys nor of what pains of jealousy lay before him. For the actor also loved women, perhaps even more than men. Was that possible? Questions and more questions — unrest, sleeplessness, delusion — hate and love all intermingled. Was it worth the effort? I was glad that I knew nothing of such a state of mind. Should I have intervened? But how? Perhaps I could have. I did have some influence over him. He might have listened to me. But I preferred to be an eyewitness and a good comrade. I had my work — that was enough.

My work was difficult but filled with quiet pleasure. My personal life was neither joyous nor quiet. Helmut had turned away from me in disillusionment because I did not want to discuss his passion with him. My master watched me suspiciously; only much later did he realize that I never had thought, even in dreams, of being his rival for Katinka of the rosy voice.

To tell the truth, I really was his rival in my dreams. But who would condemn me on that account? It became clear to me in a dream with wild, lightninglike rapture, with a flash of bloody lust (I can use only this unrestrained word), that there was something else in me than the wish for a matrimonial relationship with an older, more motherly than passionate wife. But I treated Katinka just as if she were Helmut or Karl Otto in skirts. She noticed it and fumed. What else do you expect from a very young, foolish girl about whom the housekeeper reported that she had married Kaiser chiefly (apart from his money and fame) because the name of Katinka Kaiser sounded so funny. Perhaps it would have been shrewder for me to use the infatuation of the sweet nymph (when she was swimming, I saw her from above as a really enchanting creature in her black tricot in the middle of the blue-green lake) in order to educate her. But was that my assignment? Did I not need someone in authority over myself? Did I dare yield to the urge to play fate? I was young, younger than she.

I had responsibilities enough to cause me problems, for example, to care at least a little for my half brother and sister. The twenty marks were due. Vroni reminded me of that. I took heart and went to my parents out of season; my usual visit fell on Sunday. My father had not given me the twenty-five marks as always on the first of the month because he assumed that I had no expenses that summer. He had no way of knowing that I cared for his illegitimate children — such unfortunate creatures were simply called dissolute bastards. He was collecting the initial capital for his woodwork production; my request was most inconvenient for him. He asked if I needed twenty-five marks all at once for cigarettes. Actually, cigarettes cost me nothing, for Katinka had from the beginning placed a large package of the best Turkish cigarettes next to my microscope every day. Her husband saw it but did not dare object, because he feared Katinka's wrath. But that could not interest my father. I told him that I got no money from Councillor Kaiser, for I was working off my debts to him.

"Oh, so you have debts? That is certainly nice," he said, and knocked two pieces of wood noisily together. I took them away from him and told him how large the amount was. He tore the wood out of my hands (I had taken it quite thoughtlessly so that the noise would stop) and hissed through the gaps in his teeth (he did not have the money for expensive dentures) that he would not have thought that I would incur debts in his modest name. His words irked me. He forgot, perhaps because it would be too demeaning, that he and my mother had lived for a whole year almost entirely on the money intended for me by my great-uncle. I controlled myself; I stood there as an objective observer, as an eyewitness of facts. But I remained firm; he had to give me twenty marks at least. But that I reneged on the five marks made him still more angry.

"So — five miserable marks you, scoundrel, want to throw in my face after you have ruined my reputation?" I was silent. I knew what he meant. In the petition attesting impecunity that I had had to present to avoid the fees for studying, there had been a column: Occupation of Father. I had written in: Cottager. If I had written Retired Engineering Supervisor or Manufacturer of Wood Products, my petition would have been refused. But as it was, it had gone its way to the mayor's office in S. and probably did not especially help my father's standing. My mother joined us, coughing, wiped her hands on her apron (she still perspired; that was connected to the weakness from which she had never really recovered), and admonished both of us, especially him. I took all the blame but still insisted on having the money. And I got it. Vroni was working as a housemaid; the children were in the country in the home of a poor farmer. That which my father was legally obliged to pay was not sufficient "for shirts and socks, the children were more delicate than we had thought," and I was determined to keep my word. I had done so under difficult conditions and had survived, and so had my brother and sister, who were not dissolute bastards.

At home, that is, with Kaiser in the villa, a surprise awaited me. I had been moved out. A new guest had come — the actor, Helmut's friend, who on Helmut's insistence had traveled to S. Helmut was much more relaxed, although I saw that the actor, a man of mature years with sharp, spiritual, very changeable features which in all routines seemed very childlike, did not accept him fully as a man. He seemed to be much more interested in Katinka.

Papa Kaiser, however, saw the two, Oswald Schwarz and Katinka, together without jealousy; they talked, rowed, swam, played tennis, even went hunting, although they returned with only miserable game, such as a common raven. It seemed absurd to Kaiser to be jealous of a man over thirty-five. He was blind, he did not see what he did not want to see. He thought that only his advanced age was to blame for Katinka's fickleness, and since the actor had as much gray hair as he did, and that already at thirty-five, he did not see him as a rival. Moreover, he suspected the connection between Helmut and the actor, and he did not see a brutal man in the slender artist troubled by sleeplessness and a thousand imaginary burdens — much less a ruthless wife-stealer.

Therefore he came to me very calmly in my large, bright room under the roof, sat down at the microscope and worked with me, smoking and drinking cognac. Since Katinka no longer left cigarettes for me, he finally gave me some. I did not care for any brandy.

I was still at the beginning of cranial anatomy. I had no more than twenty or thirty sections behind me, since the preparations had to be carefully investigated and not a single one passed by because it showed only slight, almost unnoticeable, variations from the preceding and following ones.

What I saw and experienced thrilled me. It thrilled me quite differently but just as deeply as the breathtaking excitement in my dream of the nude Katinka. It was day in comparison to night. It helped me. Swimming and rowing seemed much less desirable than at first. I could not part from my work. Once, in a conversation with Kaiser, I compared the arrangement of the cells, which were in a puzzling, rhythmic, orderly relationship (although no one could solve the puzzle, no one grasped the rhythm, and no one had yet discovered the plan of even a cubic millimeter), with that of the Milky Way, which I could see from my bed at night when I could not fall asleep because of the music and the laughter below on the terrace over the lake. My teacher was opposed to such comparisons. Hold strictly to that which is! His motto was to ignore everything which is not. Nerve cells were something and the Milky Way something else. He was a specialist in one and an ignoramus in the other.

In the middle of October we all moved back to the city. Kaiser took me with him in his car. Very early in the morning his wife, his children and the actor (not to forget the little dog) had gone ahead. I had hoped that during the quiet trip Kaiser would comment about my circumstances, for to be honest, I shuddered at the prospect of returning to my barren attic room, ice cold in winter, and even more to the dishwashing at the Prince Regent of Bavaria. I had even hinted to my mother before my departure. She had to know that I lived in miserable want. She had let me talk, had hesitated a long time, and then had said that if I wanted to take back "my generosity," she would tell my father so. With that, there was nothing left for me to do but to kiss her damp, trembling hand. My mother was not yet old, but she was already entirely gray and carried herself like an ancient peasant woman.

Kaiser, too, was not very obliging. But I did not give up. Even if he did not want to go along with the idea of giving me a fixed monthly salary instead of paying for individual hours of dictation, I did convince him, although with more difficulty than before, to let me have some money. I absolutely needed a hundred marks. I had earned ninety marks in the course of three months. My total debt amounted again to three hundred marks. But I simply could not appear in my old suit, which was falling to pieces. I had to have shoes and underclothes. We parted rather coolly in the city. Perhaps he had expected me to be profusely grateful.

The little attic room was cleaned up in honor of my return — everything gleamed and glistened and the custodian's wife had put a bouquet of asters on the table. I thanked her cordially, for after all she owed me nothing. I was received just as cordially in the hotel. I had been afraid that they would find a substitute for me, but the manageress had kept my place vacant; I was now a very dependable dishwasher. I did the work just as a factory worker did at his machine. Something unusual had to arise to cause me to break a piece. I did not create real devastation until the next spring, after Easter, when in the fourth semester practical exercises began in physiology, that is, experiments on living animals, vivisection.

I had known for a long time what that meant. Helmut had told me about it in the rain in our little garden. Even then I felt a severe revulsion. For a long time I had not wanted to shake hands with Dr. Kaiser (of course, he did not want to take mine either) because I thought that he had sunk his hands in the blood of creatures who were martyred for the sake of science. I could have told myself that this was part of our profession and that I would not be spared. Perhaps I did say that to myself and tried to comfort myself that it would not be so bad. Since I had been able to dissect the cadaver of the brandy-drinking brother, I certainly would not lose heart at the sight of a suffering mongrel. But I will not describe the details. I will not tell what kind of experiment it was, or how the animal behaved, or the people.

I will say only one thing: the medical profession was my only goal in life, my only ideal. But if I had known two years earlier what was involved, I would have become a tour guide or a metal worker or have sawed wood veneer. I had wanted to rule, and I had wanted to increase my knowledge. But I did not want to rule over an animal, similar to a human being, caught by a blind fate, exceptionally smart, which could suffer like a man — and perhaps in his misery even more, for he had no hope, no faith, no beautiful memories and no dream of a canine heaven.

I did not want to learn anything from such a creature. I did not want to slake my thirst for knowledge with its mechanical convulsions. Later I saw many people suffer unbearably, even the next year in the first clinical semester — at a patient's bed, on a surgical table. But I would let a human being suffer and scream, gnash his teeth, roll his eyes, and sweat cold drops from all his pores a thousand times more easily than I could an animal, for I was not to blame for his pains. Perhaps I could not help him; after all, I was only an eyewitness, eager to learn. But I was not to blame. I had no end in view. But the suffering of a dog or an even more pitiable cat — which, because it is more defiant, could twist and turn even more horribly and which could howl even more miserably because it is more intelligent — filled my heart with revulsion. I did not want to profit from this lecture. Could I do anything about it? Foolish question! The horror was stronger than reason; it was the old monster, grinding, crushing, consuming, which came over me. It was a heart, like mine, which was beating there, uncovered on the table; it was a lung which breathed like mine. I was especially revolted that it was just because of this human similarity, because of this relationship of highly civilized men to primitive animals still unchanged from prehistoric times, that the poor creature had come to his fate. Beside myself with shame and horror, I asked myself, who is the beast — man or the animal? Suddenly I remembered my dream of Katinka bathed in blood, and I was horrified. Pale as a ghost and with shaking knees, I went out into the corridor and waited until the lecture ended, got my hat, and wandered through the city for the whole afternoon. In the evening I went to work in the hotel. I broke everything that came to hand. My hands were not shaking; it was as if the devil directed them. It was then that I believed for the first time in the existence of Satan. I realized that my former view of the world had been too neat, that I had not seen much because I had not wanted to see it. And added to all my misfortunes was the fact that the smell of fat and slightly tainted venison that had left long before clung to me again. It would not leave me, and it was a hellish day. I thought of going home, fleeing to my mother in order to confide everything in her. But I was ashamed. I had decided to be a Spartan and could not even bear courageously what my comrades looked at quietly, a cigarette in their mouths and their eyes filled with a cold greed for knowledge — and curiosity. Or should I confide in the councillor?

He who because of a personal ambition to carry on a sensational experiment, and to appear as a very famous man in the eyes of one of his stupid wives when he received a scientific award or a high state award, had sacrificed hecatombs of animals — apparently in vain?

There was only one other recourse — to break off my studies, to return home and to help my father. But did I really help him when I replaced an untrained assistant but robbed him of the seventy-five marks? When I cut off the twenty marks from my half brother and sister? For my great-uncle gave me the money only for my studies and demanded the evidence each semester. What should I do? I stayed away from my lectures for three days, asked the custodian's wife to bring me a loaf of bread and a half liter of milk each day with the water supply — and I thought back and forth. Finally I found a kind of solution: I rationalized my problem. I decided that when I finally became a doctor, I would exert all my powers to limit vivisection, which in a small measure was indispensable, to the minimum, to anesthetize the animals in every case, and to provide funds to bear the extra cost of this humane treatment. I believed in progress, in humanity, because I had to. But that was not enough. I decided that henceforth I would eat no more meat, and I remained a vegetarian up to the time of the war.

In the eyes of someone who understood people, like Kaiser, I had always been considered a cold-blooded person, controlling well any instinctive reactions. I was skillful with my hands, and he advised me strongly to prepare myself in surgery, which was useful to every doctor, even a future psychiatrist, as a stern test of character. Following his wishes, I volunteered for unpaid service during the summer in the university surgical clinic instead of going along to S. For weeks I had night duty — watching, learning, busy with little manual chores, assisting the surgeon of the day, an experienced assistant in the absence of the professor.

I have to confess that I was uncertain. I had an interest in surgery, the most active of the medical branches, but I also had an equally strong interest in psychiatry and nerve therapeutics, which was the least effective branch in relationship to healing. But I would have been happiest if I could have turned to the universal, very effective but not especially bloody, internal medicine – the treatment of the inner organs, of metabolic disturbances, of infectious diseases, poisonings, tuberculosis, tropical diseases, and so forth. At that time it was making glorious, stormy progress, particularly because everything previously known was being questioned as a result of Roentgen's experimentation. It was linked to no country, to no language, as psychiatry, the knowledge of sick souls (soul and language are almost the same), was, and it was not as impersonal as surgery, which knows people only from the physical point of view.

But I was indebted to Kaiser, and not only for heavy financial contributions. In the last years of my studies he had granted me a minimum stipend. And more, much more, he had become a second father to me. He had maintained himself as such and had drawn closer to me step by step while my natural father had become more and more estranged in an ununderstandable fashion – and really without any basis.

At the end of my studies I spent a semester as a volunteer assistant in the surgical clinic. An unexpected experience made it clear that I did not lack coldness, objectivity, and self-control. One night, a young butcher's apprentice, unconscious from shock and loss of blood, was brought in. He had received a deep wound in the hip joint in a scuffle. He was anesthetized and the joint disinfected. We immediately began to enlarge the ragged wound carefully in order to grasp and quickly tie off the cut blood vessels. But the bleeding grew worse as the operation progressed. A very large blood vessel in the lower layers must have been cut. That wound needed to be found shortly or the poor fellow would bleed to death. But how to find it? Blood was literally all that we could see. His face was white as a sheet and everything was soaked in hot red. We could feel around carefully with a finger in the depths, but how could fingers encased in rubber gloves and cloth gloves over them find a blood vessel in the many layers of tissue and then find the injured spot on the blood vessel?

A highly gifted surgeon could perhaps have found it by intuition and performed a miracle – but we? If it were not found, however, we would have to stop the operation and bandage him – not in the hope that such a bandage would stop the bleeding and save his life, even if it were applied with the most professional skill. But only in order to take the patient to his ward still living so that he would not die on the operating table, something which could create problems for the clinic, that is, in terms of records, legal investigations, and the like.

When all of us — the surgeon of the day, his first assistant, I as second assistant, and the anesthetist — were at the end of our rope, I had an idea. I had been reading professional magazines very carefully and remembered a new method designed by a medical officer by the name of M——b. In cases like this one, he took an ordinary piece of gas tubing, rolled it around the patient's belly, and then pulled it tight until the large blood vessels of the abdomen were compressed. Then there was a lack of blood in the legs; no blood came from the heart; none returned to the heart. With this absence of blood, one could see clearly and could find the wounded spot and open it. Once it was exposed, the vessel could be cut off and the patient saved — assuming that it was not the great artery of the thigh, the indispensable source of the circulatory system, without which the leg would be dead.

These considerations were irrelevant. We were not concerned with the localized death but with death itself. The surgeon listened to my idea rather skeptically. But since there was no other solution, no miracle — perhaps, too, because I, in spite of my youth and inexperience, knew how to direct him a little — he sent for some gas tubing and laid it around the abdomen of the slender, skinny young man. An operating room assistant pulled to the right and an old stoic sister pulled to the left. In twenty seconds the effect was apparent, as if by magic. The bleeding had stopped. In another thirty seconds we found the wound — but it was on the main thigh artery. To tie off the vessel meant to rescue his life but to sacrifice the leg; it would have to be amputated sooner or later. But amputation is a kind of a disgrace for a surgeon, like pulling a tooth for a dentist. It is a last resort.

The American doctor Armand Carell had made a second important technical discovery, a particular technique for sewing the blood vessels. Very thin needles were necessary; we had none. But the sister who busied herself with embroidery in her leisure time had some. They were brought and sterilized for two minutes;

the finest thread was used; the seams were joined as it had been described in the *International Surgical Review* for doctors throughout the world.

We were fortunate to be able to match the ends of the wound exactly, since it had been caused by a sharp instrument, probably a sharpened pocket knife such as farmers, butchers, and lumbermen like to carry in a small pocket above their buttocks. The gas tubing had to be taken off quickly, for the body would not tolerate it for long. But we risked it. We had to risk it — the test had to be made to determine if we had cheated death of a human life. We saw how the limp vessel, no larger than a quill, began to fill with throbbing blood. The seams were distended, but they held. The rest of the operation was child's play. We all worked well together and left the operating room bathed in sweat but contented.

The young butcher's apprentice continued to cause us trouble. The blood circulation had been disturbed too much; gangrene developed in his toes so that the first joint of the big toe and of two others had to be taken off. It seemed to be a cheap price for avoiding certain death. But that was not his opinion, and the clinic had to pay him indemnities because he was handicapped in his work and, further, he viewed the reconstruction of his feet to be a scar.

But we had not anticipated any particular gratitude. We thought of ourselves as demigods who do not labor for thanks.

But I remained loyal to Kaiser, who had prescribed psychiatry for me; he carried a heavy burden — and he needed me.

The two technical advances which had saved the life of the butcher's apprentice would never have been possible without long and systematic experimentation on animals. Therefore I had to adapt myself to these experiments, since they were still indispensable. At that time a human life was so valuable that one could set it against an innumerable mass of animal existences and conclude that the human life was the highest good that the earth possesses.

This thought made the plans of the councillor acceptable to me. I did not believe with any fanaticism in the idea that he had — that is, to achieve a cure for the mentally ill or retarded by transferring the tissue parts of the thyroid gland of a healthy person to the patient. He bragged ahead of time, "I will make an intelligent person out of a cretin."

But it was good that, of two researchers, one was a fanatic and ignored all obstacles, while the other was concerned about good technical procedures, checked everything, and arrived at an objective, incontestable conclusion. I was supposed to be that one.

At first we were not concerned with healing real mental illnesses, which left everyone helpless because it was known only rather vaguely that the brain was the seat of the suffering. How, where, and why were not clear to anyone in the case of the most important mental illnesses. Was the normal functioning of the brain, thinking, clear to a cranial researcher?

Here the most ingenious intuition of a divinely favored scholar and doctor did not help. All systematizing had remained fruitless. In the course of my studies I had had innumerable cranial sections under my microscope, and Kaiser had had even more. But if we had had to summarize what we knew about the seat of the spirit and its mechanics we would have had to remain silent, smiling skeptically in the midst of the piles of sections and the bundles of reports. Perhaps my romantic view five years earlier — that the arrangement of the ganglia resembled the appearance of the Milky Way — was just as exact as what we knew about the seat of speech, about the center of these or those muscular movements, if one did not prefer to remain silent.

The old scholar was driven to talk more often than he liked. He wanted to keep his secret, which had not been a secret for a long time. And yet everything had been so human, so banal, so common, that Kaiser had to be overwhelmed by a passion which prevented him from recognizing at once the pattern and the inevitable outcome: an old man, a young woman — that was all.

This old man had once been young. This gray-haired Romeo begging for tenderness had once been loved. He who felt so lonely had three splendid sons and two almost grown, beautiful daughters. But did that comfort him? He wanted to stay young and handsome, irresistible, eternal in spite of a withering body; he wanted to be loved. He did not want to lose the demigod halo around his bony, bald, Caesarlike skull.

Katinka did not love him. She said so quite openly. He did not believe her and twisted her words. The housekeeper, a somewhat maturer but still handsome woman who was divorced through no fault of her own, with whom I had become intimate, told me about it when I asked her. She and I were not unhappy with each other. Everything fit together, perhaps because we expected so little of each other. There is nothing more to be said about it. We were both attached to the old man. We wondered how we could open his eyes. But how did one open the eyes of an extraordinarily intelligent, creative man, who as a doctor had certainly given many who had lost their balance the advice which he now withheld from himself?

He still had a trace of hope. I do not know if it was really so or if he imagined it. The actor whom Katinka loved — not considering that Katinka Schwarz did not sound as droll as Katinka Kaiser — was also on the descent. He failed to get important roles, and in the little ones he received he was a disappointment. For to be great in an insignificant role is difficult. He was in need, had several people to support, and was made older rather than rejuvenated by his new love.

Kaiser imagined that if he could announce one day a world-shaking scientific discovery, Katinka would love him again the next. He had never been able to bring himself to consider that there might be women who in fact did not love him even though he honored them with his love. He therefore thought that if he came home from Stockholm with the citation of a Nobel Prize, Katinka would throw her arms around him, kiss his withered lips, and Mr. Schwarz would be forgotten because he was a second-rate actor. This illusion kept him upright.

In the course of the years he had carried on many different experiments, but they had all disappointed him. One cannot do experiments which involve the mind on animals and other forms of life that do not possess emotions and mentality. Then he had an ingenious idea, and I was to assist him. He offered to divide his fame with me — and when he would give up his activity at the height of his fame in order to live solely for his wife with the rosy voice, I would be his successor. He promised me this often. This was why he had helped to train me in surgery. "I'll make an intelligent person out of every cretin," he repeated day after day in the family circle, and believed that he was making an impression on

Katinka, who was beginning to fade. In the company of two aging men she was no longer gay and childlike.

We went to work, first with a cretin who had been entrusted to Kaiser's institution by his mother. Kaiser persuaded the mother to come to the sanatorium to be operated on at the same time as her dwarfed idiot son, who at twenty years of age was only four feet tall, and who as a result of edema could stammer only a few words and had no bodily control. I was at one table to take a part of the thyroid gland from the mother under anesthesia; Kaiser was at a table next to me to transplant this piece into a small incision in the neck of the poor mental cripple. There was no danger involved. It was interesting, in any case.

Before the operation the boy had been so backward that he could not even count the fingers of one hand. What joy there was when, a few days after the operation, the animal-like, dreary look of the cretin became brighter and more human! The boy grew, he gained in a few months as much as ten centimeters. His strawlike hair became silky; he spoke a hundred and sixty to seventy words, could count to twenty, could tell time. He recognized his mother, who was almost beside herself with joy. We began to teach him to read and to write. He began to eat like an adult, and he also began to sing to himself in a pleasant voice. He had become a human being.

The happiness which Kaiser felt at this time was so magnetic, irresistible, elementary, that his sweet little wife was affected, and the old man, even before there were any public honors, received evidence of a greater tenderness in kisses, caresses, pet names, and adoring glances. Only I remained skeptical. I thought that it was still, maybe even more so, only the reactions of a daughter — and the prompting of a conscience that had not let her be at peace in the face of the sufferings of her husband. She let it appear as the tenderness of a young woman only recently awakened. One could deceive himself about it, but one ought not to let it happen.

What I know, however, is that the progress in the physical and spiritual growth of the young cretin soon stopped. He gradually forgot his new skills, with no recall. He became what he had been before. The intoxication of the thyroid gland was spent. He had been awake; then he slept again. His mother and Kaiser did not see it. I saw it in the clinical behavior of the poor fellow; I saw it in a test excision from the transplanted gland — it had become useless fat. The scientific revolution amounted to nothing. What could Kaiser do? He did something ugly; he explained that out of envy I had falsified his results or had been deliberately careless in the operation.

The old man, who to me resembled God, was especially irked that I had been able to avoid by virtue of will power, sobriety and self-control such weaknesses of the flesh as he had revealed again and again, and that I had advised him to do the same. "What does a vegetarian know of meat?" he cried out scornfully. But perhaps one of us learned something about the flesh, "the impure vessel of man and woman," in the process of mastering himself.

He was right, however, in asserting that I did not love as he did and did not want to be loved as he was. I wanted to live my whole life in the cool light of conscious reason. Perhaps I had to suffer immeasurably later because of this attitude, because I could not comprehend, or did not want to, that not everything is enclosed in reason. There is a spirit, a soul. There are also satanic drives. In decisive moments it is not logical reason, not the spirit of La Rochefoucauld nor of Voltaire which determines our convictions and conclusions, but incalculable shifts of feeling.

So I could have logically drawn from the facts the conclusion that I had protected my chief from dangerous errors by means of my objective decision in two important aspects of his life, wife and profession, and that he ought to thank me. And even if he did not want to thank me, and if he, in keeping with the maxim of the Kaiser-Jew, substituted meanness for gratitude, he did not need, after the lapse of so many years, to remind me of my father's corruption. That was absurd, really not worthy of him. For what did that have to do with me? But I recognized his evil purpose and resigned. I had developed a taste for psychiatry, its new methodology which battled the sickness of the mind with mental means — analysis, hypnosis. I still owed him considerable money. For the moneys received I gave him a note which he tore to pieces, beside himself in anger. I picked up the scraps of paper, quietly put them in an envelope, sealed it, and left it on his desk. He looked at me uncomprehendingly as I left his laboratory. Angelica, the housekeeper, appalled by his behavior, also gave notice. And as if his life had not been sufficiently disturbed, Katinka told him that same evening that she could not live without Oswald. She did not want to deceive her husband. (Perhaps he would have preferred that to losing her entirely.) She asked him to grant her the divorce that he had forced on so many unwilling wives. She wanted no alimony. He asked, "And how will you live, you silly paupers?" She shrugged her shoulders. He accepted her refusal of money, not because of stinginess and niggardliness, but out of meanness so they would not be happy.

They left that same evening with a little trunk. He stayed at home for the next few days, sitting at the telephone, waiting for a call from her or from me. He thought that both of us would have to come back, but he thought of us only in anger and resentment. I had gone to my parents. My father had built a small factory for the Swedish houses; his affairs moved forward slowly but firmly. He still had that certain sweet modesty which made his presence unpleasant to me. My mother was stooped and her face wrinkled; there was something austere and awe-inspiring about her as well as something intimate and genuine — and I felt good with her.

After a few days the housekeeper hunted me up. She came in Kaiser's name; he wanted me to come back and to forget everything. He had also forgiven Katinka. When I saw him again I was shocked, for he was the ruin of someone who in his own way had been a strong person. His beard showed great reddened gaps around his lips; in his emotional delirium he had pasted adhesive tape over his mouth in order to control the outbursts of pain, to learn to be silent, to learn restraint. It was a senile pathological gesture "against wine, against weeping," he said with a broken voice. He showed me the draft of a letter to his beloved Katinka, in which he promised to make her his sole heir, "as the thanks of my heart for all beauty and love." I told him that this excessive generosity would appear to her as an insult; rather, he should provide the couple with a few hundred marks a month and forget them.

He struggled to follow my advice. He pretended to be without jealousy, to have only a paternal good will. However, I saw his eyes flame up in passionate wildness, in spite of his years, when he read in the paper that "the trained, and merely trained, court theater actor, the retired O. Schwarz, had proved all those wrong who had overrated him so foolishly and had showered him with gold and laurel." "Oh, the poor girl! Not even Oswald anymore. O. Schwarz! If she reads that!" said Kaiser, handing me the sheet. He beamed. He was almost young again. It was his first joy in a long time.

Of course, a few months later he was again in deepest despair. Not because anything special had happened, but just because nothing had happened, and he found it difficult to endure the irrevocable course of the facts of getting old, of resignation and of loneliness.

The housekeeper, who like me had returned at his request, had had good connections at court for a long time. The old man had received sufficient honors in his lifetime. I found it difficult to imagine that being ennobled would mean anything to him. But it was nonetheless true. The difficulties were great, because Kaiser had the reputation in upper circles of being a poor Catholic and half anarchistic. But he changed in a day. The throne, the army, the altar were suddenly his most sacred possessions. He who had learned to value the great achievements of Jewish scholars, by whom the purely mental methodology had been especially strengthened, suddenly became a Jew-baiter, because Schwarz was the son of a half-Jewish mixed marriage. He imagined that Schwarz would be pale with envy when he discovered that Kaiser had been raised to the peerage. With trembling lips he repeated to himself a thousand times the name of his former wife, Katinka von Kaiser, and asked me again and again if it did not have a beautiful sound. I nodded, smiling. "And on the other side Kat Schwarz," he sneered, using the common custom of shortening women's names — for example, Ma, Kat, Lu, Pat, Li, Lo.

All these episodes brought him contentment for only a few weeks. He was tired of life. Working for the public meant nothing to him. He despised politics as the wrestling arena of the most common instincts and as the course of the most banal intrigues. He told me that he wanted to join a monastery, adding with a bitter smile, yes, a monastery for atheists. "And your family?" I asked, for I thought of Helmut. He did not deign to answer me.

I was supposed to take over the clinic, but first he wanted me to get an academic degree. For that I had to present a scientific work, a dissertation. As a rule they are useless compilations, busy-work. I set a higher goal for myself. I was interested in a symptom which was being more thoroughly studied under the direction of the young Jewish Viennese school of psychiatry and of Charcot: hysteria and the disturbances created by the mind called psychogenic disorders, which were partly of a mechanical nature such as disorders in walking, partly of a more mental nature such as hysterical blindness, hysterical deafness, hysterical loss of speech, muteness, loss of feeling. Finding a way from the everyday spirit to the innermost soul was the procedure. Hypnosis and analysis promised much. But there was no single certain procedure. I gathered much material, and my work was a better compilation than most. I presented it finally and achieved my doctorate.

This area which reached into the depths of the soul, was also interesting for legal decrees, since psychogenic disorders were linked to simulations. I became something of a specialist in this area.

At that time it became suddenly apparent to me that there is really no basic difference between fate and chance. There were two people named Oswald Schwarz: the second was no educated, blasé, delicate wife-stealer, but a silent, malicious, faded vagabond living in misery. He had been accused of the robbery-murder of a fellow vagabond in a hostel, then he claimed to have become suddenly blind. The matter was not clear, for the vagabond had wandered around for a long time after the deed as if he were out of his mind. He had finally returned to the scene of the action with bloodstained clothing and in his pocket a blood-spattered fragment with which he had cut the throat of his companion in the hostel. He was arrested, talked nonsense, fell into a deep sleep for twenty-four hours, and then never saw again.

Unapproachable, grimly brooding, he crouched in a corner of his cell with his knees drawn up, almost immobile; he did not eat except for what was shoved into his mouth. He had to be led to the hearing, for a walk, to the toilet. He tapped his way through the corridors of the jail like a blind person, bumping into everything, so that his body was covered with black and blue bruises. Kaiser as a well-known alienist was to give an expert opinion of the case.

I have always been opposed to the role of the doctor as an aide of the law. He should support the patient, standing alongside him, or he should be above him as an objective witness, but he should never be against him. He should serve the patient or be a judge of science. But others should render judgment. Nonetheless, the testimony of a doctor is sometimes a necessity in safeguarding personal freedom, I concede, just as vivisection is sometimes a bitter blessing for a society which wants its possessions safeguarded. I have an inner compulsion to recognize the interests of both parties, to understand the opposite viewpoint, to discover it.

Kaiser took me along to the examinations. He saw at once that the blindness was a psychogenic disorder, a simulation from a hysterical cause. But that truth did not suffice, I thought. I examined the patient much more carefully, almost against the will of the councillor, who had become very impatient and fidgety. I found my suspicions corroborated — Oswald Schwarz had all the earmarks of genuine epilepsy; he obviously had committed the deed in a semiconscious epileptic state. His blindness could be healed by means of hypnosis, but the epilepsy would remain.

Could an experienced psychiatrist like Kaiser fail to see that? Certainly not. He finally had to accept my diagnosis as I presented the facts to him from my records. He took the papers out of my hand. When, however, he saw the name of the vagabond — here the fate of Oswald sided with chance — he became furious, threw the diagnosis on the table, and had the clerk record only the brief comment that the blindness was hysterical. He said nothing about the patient's general condition. He could not overlook the coincidence that the poor mental cripple bore the same name as the man who had robbed him of his life's happiness. He, in his godlike state, did not testify to a false diagnosis. No. He was correct in a literal sense, for the court was primarily concerned with the blindness. If the blindness was simulated (that was the view of the Royal Bavarian public prosecutor), then all the behavior after the deed was also simulated — the return to the scene of action was motivated by a desire to pick up more or to wipe out the results of the murder by arson. The case was tried before a jury of peasants, simple souls, to whom property was everything. Oswald Schwarz had many thefts, many deeds of violence, as well as of immorality, on his record. There was no long discussion; he was quickly condemned to die. He was executed on July 30, 1914. That too was accident, fate. If the executioner had delayed a few days longer in carrying out the judgment, Oswald Schwarz would probably have been pardoned, as many others were, in the excitement of the first days of the war.

At one blow, there was no longer a Europe. Boundaries were sealed, and blood flowed all over — in the North, in the East, in the South, in the West. Cosmopolitanism was at an end. There were no more trips abroad; there were no more individual rights, no freedom of the press, therefore no freedom of thought, no freedom of research. No criticism. No reason. Only military law prevailed, the law of necessity — that is, no law! Universal international law was superseded by the sacred law of the individual nation defending itself, which fought against one or more other nations who likewise defended themselves. If they defended themselves against all the others, they could just as well have stayed at home. But they did not want to do that, even if it had been still possible. The bestial impulses, the satanic soul had been awakened; hearts which remained unmoved like iron in the midst of streaming blood, in horrible suffering and pain, were lauded, spirits which were untouched by any pain or any wounds. All were healthy, courageous and good, all were patriotic, all were proud of their nation. A saccharine wave of sentimentality united young and old, poor and rich at the feet of the altar of the threatened virtuous fatherland. Everyone gave his mite. The important and the rich gave a little, the insignificant and the poor also gave a little. Smiling coldly or with affectionate tears, the people of all countries read the reports of their armies which told of thousands of dead, ten thousand wounded, hundreds of thousands taken captive in a day, for example, on the occasion of the Battle of the Marne, or on the occasion of the "righteous destruction" of the Serbs. No one hoped for anything except victory.

But what then? What were the goals of the war? "That will be the subject of discussion when we have brought our infamous opponents to their knees" was the answer, simple in its intent, verbose in its form. There were no tangible goals. And how could goals be maintained in this chaos when before, in apparent order, the masses had no goals — other than, perhaps, warm food, good shelter, much amusement and a long, comfortable life? But since all Europeans had these goals and the war could bring them to only one side in the event of victory in the best sense, the outcome was clear from the beginning to any logically thinking person. But the individual was nothing anymore. The state needed masses, the last man, and the last men became great by addition and they considered themselves lords, even though they were slaves.

It depended on the masses — and one spoke to them. Unending propaganda began. A fertile and satisfactory lie was, in the service of a good cause, better than a bitter and sad truth; for example, everyone, friend and foe, wanted to be the victim of an unjust attack. Reason and restraint, which make a human being human, suddenly were considered inimical to the fatherland: "Thinking is forbidden by the police! Until victory be silent, endure, keep your mouth shut!" At first a few objected. For any length of time — no one. Whether everyone had a soul remained open to question, but everyone had a satanic soul. Everyone wanted to be stronger, and as the stronger, therefore, in the right. Victory was the right and stoicism the law of all.

As time moved on, the whole nation entered into war service, which gradually included everything in its jaws and which never gave up anything. No more great and small; everything was valuable in the mass, valueless singly. Whether an attack was worth a hundred thousand lives or "only" ten thousand was determined by the strategic situation. None of the people who died was asked. All swore an oath because to refuse to swear was suicide. All obeyed. This was their honor. A few technicians conducted the war, technicians who were specialists and who did not trouble themselves as to why it was happening and when or how it would end. There were only strategic, political goals — no moral, religious ends. The nation was God. Everyone was assigned a place — there he had to stay, to work or to shoot or to labor in a factory. Most people were glad, however, that they were not asked. Such passive obedience dulled worries, conscience, fear about life. No one had any rest and no one had a right to it.

Self-defense, the law of necessity for the state, demanded that everyone be a means to an end. I too. Never did I have so much to do, nor so much will to do it – and never did I accomplish so little.

At first I was in Councillor Kaiser's service because he had listed me as indispensable with the General Command and so kept me from military service. Together with his elderly senior doctor, I supervised his institution until the difficulties in getting food and the lack of trained, dependable caretakers made it impossible for us to keep the patients. They were sent either to regional institutions or to sanatoriums in the country, where obtaining supplies was less difficult than in the city. The state, with all its power and authority, could neither guarantee its subjects life and the maintenance of existence nor protect people – husband, wife, old man, child, sick and healthy – from hunger, cold, nakedness. But it was all the more puffed up.

My father continued to live in S. His factory had switched to making war materiel and produced musket stocks. The necessary raw materials became poorer by the day; since, however, it was a part of the weapon which did not receive rough use, he managed and even increased his production with a few more workers. But then – for the sake of appearance, not with any joy – he had to invest his modest profits in war loans. He was afraid of being drafted even at his age, and therefore was doubly patriotic – proud of his son, proud of his factory and proud of his victorious countrymen.

Even the old Kaiser-Jew had put his weak powers at the disposal of his fatherland and went from one hospital to the other in a shabby black civilian suit, but wearing on his chest the Iron Cross that he had received as a volunteer in 1870–1871. The young doctors were needed at the front. His daughter had married a Socialist deputy, a leader of the workers, Leon Lazarus. This intelligent and experienced man had not escaped the general infection of the war mania; he had volunteered and been accepted, although as a deputy he could not be drafted. He lacked neither conviction nor courage. I later learned that he had volunteered for the Western Front in order to escape from the conflict between his international pacifist convictions and his duty as a German national. Fate was not troubled by his reasons. He was good cannon fodder and fell in his first battle. His widow, lovelier than ever in her sorrow, suffered greatly, but she was silent, bore everything, and became a nurse in a troop hospital after she had completed a course of study.

I too was called up. As a young student I had not been considered of military caliber because my ribs were somewhat deformed, and the state laid great worth on perfect soldiers. Later it was no longer so choosy. I therefore went along with the training, spoke no unnecessary word, and stoically bore all the exercises. I again resumed reading my old La Rochefoucauld and studied French in my free time, for all probability pointed to my going to the Western Front. Angelica, with whom I had been living for years, had to give up her position as receptionist and housekeeper for Kaiser. She had some money and against my wishes (it was our first quarrel) she put it in war loans because these carried a high interest and seemed safer than pure gold. She planned to become a housekeeper supervisor in an officers' hospital, but she wanted to devote herself solely to me as long as I was behind the lines. She spoke an almost perfect French, and we began to converse very formally in that language. Maybe that was the root of our gradual estrangement. Maybe I was influenced by the inhumanity of the time, by the fact that I had been torn out of my profession and was without hope or goal so that I was no longer capable of experiencing a harmonious relationship such as we had always had. In any case, she was reconciled to her divorced husband before he went off to battle.

I was attached to her, to be sure, but I could feel little regret. Everything was frozen and dulled in me, and I longed for the day when I would leave and become a junior field doctor. My mother went to every length to make me change my mind. There would have been plenty of ways to insure a safe little place in the hinterlands or at least on a base for me, but I wanted none of them.

As a young doctor I had been a good surgeon, so when I was asked what specialties I had, I named surgery first and nerve therapy second. I was, therefore, not surprised that I was ordered to the Western Front in the section of La Fierte Lescoudes to serve in a divisional hospital of an area hotly embattled and completely destroyed.

I arrived late in the evening, and almost immediately I had to begin the first operation. Since the field hospital was very close to the front lines, those wounded who needed immediate surgery came to us. Therefore we did mostly amputations. The wounded were classified, and there was little time for consideration of either the doctor or the wounded. It was better to live as a cripple than to die — everyone accepted that fact.

The heavy battles in this sector suddenly abated; for several months we had almost nothing to do. Then the cannon thunder swelled to an uninterrupted booming; the earth shuddered. French planes buzzed low over our white operating tents marked with huge red crosses, but they dropped no bombs. In less than an hour the first ambulances began to roll in, filled at several levels with the badly wounded. We experienced six weeks of uninterrupted gigantic attack. We never undressed. Except for a few hours of restless sleep, for which we took off only our socks and shoes, we stood at one of the many operating tables and literally waded in blood. As the smell of fat had enveloped me when I was a hungry student, so now it was the smell of bloody human flesh.

The operations never stopped; it was a continuous chain, arousing horror. We never saw a human face, for it lay under a white chloroform mask. We did not make a decision — everything was predetermined. The soldiers, both troops and officers, came to us with no distinctions, all ready and anesthetized on an automated belt — to apply the analogy of Henry Ford's method to our human operating. We worked quickly and surely, just like experienced factory workers.

After a few weeks I was stupefied, brutish, without energy and yet always tense, not able to read a letter or to write, to follow the reports of the army, to take up a book or in the occasional break to play cards or to listen to the gramophone. Operating on and on, cutting the skin in a circle after application of the ligature, cutting off the blood, holding the upper blood vessels, separating the muscles and blood vessels and nerve strands in one smooth cut, grasping the bone saw and sawing with lightning speed. And then a limb fell; it was quickly removed. For time was money or more than money, time was human lives; and even if the state no longer valued human lives, it did not want anyone to die too early, for he might be usable later on. Then came the careful search for the deep veins and tying them off. They were always where they were supposed to be. Then taking care of the stump, important especially in upper thigh amputations. Then cleaning the wound, the skin suture – and quickly on to the next. After arms and hands came more arms and hands or lower thighs or upper thighs – and that went on for many weeks.

Most of us doctors began to drink a lot; I did not. The food was good and plentiful, but everything tasted of amputation. Our work was humane and necessary. As we helped others, so we had to be helped by good comrades.

Our lives were not safe. Heavy missiles fell once into our operating barracks. I was not present; I had summoned my last bit of energy and had gone for a ride in a little cart in the beautiful clear weather. My comrades – doctors, nurses, chaplains, orderlies and cooks – were badly wounded or killed just like soldiers and officers. It was unavoidable. It could not even be proved that "the Englishman" to whom the heavy artillery, a sea battery, belonged had attacked the hospital on purpose. Substitutions were quickly made, and the next day I operated with all new material and with colleagues previously unknown to me. But in any case the doctors changed often. No one could endure it for long; I was one of the toughest. Alcohol helped them only for a time and damaged their working capacity – morphine was even worse.

I forced myself, and thanks to my will power I stayed away from both. When the work diminished a little, they tried to cheer us up, strengthen our patriotism, and turn our thoughts. Improvised stages were set up a few kilometers behind the front lines, and little troupes of actors played as well as they could, usually with haste and pale with fear behind their heavy makeup. At such a performance I saw Oswald Schwarz. He was almost unrecognizable. He had become fat and bloated, had changed from being a character actor to a comedian, and had developed in his new field far enough that he made his listeners, troops and officers, laugh.

I could not endure it and left. A colleague invited me to accompany him to the officers' bordello. I went along but was disgusted by the sight of the women, just as I was with myself – and I left.

The battle at this sector was at an end and in our favor. The sanitation troop packed our materials in numbered cases, broke up, and set up their tents a few kilometers forward. We did not have to wait long for work. The French mounted a counterattack, and again there were four weeks of continuous operating. Then it was claimed that this sector was not important; it did not merit such a great sacrifice of people. We packed up and withdrew to the spot which we had left just a few weeks before. I was given a furlough because I was next in line. The bureaucracy functioned well. We were always cared for, and the quality of the medicinal materials grew worse only gradually to the same degree as the human material.

I found my parents. They were both happy — my father this time almost more than my mother, I thought. I had lost my inner balance; I could hardly carry on a conversation. No one wanted truthful reports, only sunny, hopeful, soldierly, Spartan stories. It was not a question of discussion. I saw Victoria again. I stared at her and she at me. I stared at her because of her beauty and she at me as if I were a strange animal.

On the home front a remarkable mood was prevalent, in part senselessly excited, in part senselessly doubtful. The masses, even in distant spots, began to learn to know the war at first hand. Several peace advocates spoke courageously of a peace without victors and losers, of an end to the fighting without annexations and war damages. They accomplished nothing. The state, which could do nothing but stubbornly fight on because it had no certain goal except to maintain itself and to grow stronger than it had been, threw tremendous counterpropaganda into the battle for attitudes. Although the friends of peace had a great majority in the parliament, they had to succumb since they did not have the executive power. This was held by a man responsible to no one,* a dictator of the rank of marshal, whom everyone had to obey blindly, without thinking, without hesitation. Since personally he was blameless, and like his assistants lived only for victory and accomplished immeasurable work, he was trusted, and the people clung to him as if he were both fate and God.

I returned to the front. But I rebelled from the depths of my heart at supporting by my knowledge and skill as a doctor something

* Paul von Hindenburg.

which I abhorred — and for whose success I had no faith. Or was there another reason that drove me to volunteer for the regular army rather than the medical corps?

Was it perhaps the satanic soul which wanted to come to the surface in me? Had I tasted blood (certainly blood had often spurted into my face), and did I want to be one of those who knew what it meant to kill someone instead of waiting behind the lines to try to correct what had been deliberately mutilated at the front? What sense is there in rescuing people from death when the state returns them to battle almost before they recuperate? Amputees, of course, did not get back to the front. But they were methodically exercised, prepared for a vocation, provided with the best artificial limbs. On the base, at home, they made themselves useful and thus freed other men to become cannon fodder. Even women were inducted with the same idea. But I have to admit that all that was not the reason. I was drawn, all of my energy urged me on, to something against which my reason rebelled. What good is it to want to clarify by means of logical reason what comes forth out of the incalculable waverings of innermost feelings? I participated with shock troops, freed from boring trench service and sentry duty, in more than one hand-to-hand battle with a few dependable, cold-blooded, courageous comrades at my side. More than once by day and by night I attacked, leading my men. I threw hand grenades. I sat by machine guns and heard the water in the cooler and moved its wooden handle (perhaps produced by my father) back and forth and was not afraid of death. I had not only become a good storm trooper myself, but my people were so devoted to me that they would have followed me to certain death without blinking an eyelash. I looked at them, nothing more. No one ever refused. Not all officers were so successful. Often as a doctor I had persuaded patients better by suggestion or by hypnosis than Kaiser. That was all to the good now.

As long as I was not in personal combat with the enemy (Indian troops, Gurkhas, were opposite us), everything was simple. Technical battle, conducted from a distance, creates no problems. But you have to experience once what the other is, what our ancestors of centuries ago knew and loved; you have to advance rejoicing in battle with a bared bayonet. You have to push forward over the crunching sandbags, with hand grenades in your fists, one in the right, one in the left; you have to feel the barbed wire tearing at your trousers and thick puttees; you have to shudder because of the indescribable feeling and at the same time long to grasp the gigantic brown-skinned fellow with a turban on his head, dressed impeccably in khaki, and struggle with him if the hand grenade thrown at him does not explode. While he stoops a little in order to be able to throw his grenade, you have to tear the bayonet fixed on your right shoulder down, you have to bore him with a skillful stab of the bayonet at the right place between the ribs. You have to hear him scream in his foreign guttural language, see him grow pale, and see how his eyes with the gigantic yellowish white around the pupils roll — how he reaches forward, how his hands are bloodily cut in his effort to pull the bayonet out — while you turn it in the wound with effort and force it deeper into the body so that the encounter will come to a speedy end — with him dead and you on to another. You have to experience how his dying, paralyzed body weighs down the bayonet so heavily that you feel it in the shoulder, know his head sinks down, and eventually you pull out the bayonet, follow your comrades who have gone ahead through new holes in the barbed wire, and then repeat this two or three more times. What I describe is only the external consequences. The monster, grinding, crushing, consuming, the splendid bestiality, the barbaric happiness and intoxication cannot be described. In a quiet room one cannot write down the words so that someone else alone in another quiet room, his cigar in his mouth, his dog at his feet, can understand this and then know how one feels.

No one experiences this by himself. I experienced it only as one in a crowd. My men were in front of me, they were next to me, they were behind me. If one fell, the others were always there. One died, but life continued. I was a good shock troop leader, perhaps too dogged and reckless, and I had many losses among my people, elite soldiers. My captain, who fastened the Iron Cross on my left side, often restrained me and warned me. But I was driven. One night I was wounded by a stray bullet. In battles at a distance I have no good fortune. A shot in the lungs. No danger to life, no consequences, no crippling. If it had not been that cursed right side, it would have been a matter of only a few weeks. But as it was, I had to go back of the lines. What struck me in the difficult treating of the wound was that I felt little pain. It was the old place; actually, I should have had more pain than I did as a young person, but I felt almost nothing. Usually doctors are very sensitive to their own suffering. I was praised for my endurance and accepted it phlegmatically.

When I was well, I received a recuperation furlough. But I wanted to work. Recuperation was impossible at this time — the beginning of 1918. I wanted to serve. They searched through my personal record and discovered to their astonishment that I was also a specialist in mental and nervous diseases. I was transferred to an institution reserved for such cases in P.* in North Germany. At the same time I was promoted out of sequence to staff doctor. At first I wrote no one about it and no letter reached me. Then gradually I began to return to my earlier existence.

I was assigned to the reserve hospital in P. where I treated numerous war casualties — not amputees, but those emotionally crippled who could not be helped by systematic exercise and ingenious false limbs. There were just as many genuine patients as there were simulators, serious mental illnesses in the early stages, hysteria at its worst, and I could continue the studies that I had begun in Kaiser's institution.

Outside, the war continued on many fronts with unchanged intensity — if anything, even more violently than before. Sometimes it seemed that faith in the final victory was waning among the people. The attempts to penetrate the Western Front after days of intense bombardment did not stop. The bombardment was difficult for a healthy person to endure, much less anyone who was nervous, sensitive, hysterical, neurasthenic. It cost unimaginable sacrifices of men and materiel and accomplished nothing.

Men came to us who held their hands over their ears because they could still hear the rumbling of heavy mortars; others saw the spurting fire of flame throwers in front of them; others staggered as if the earth shook; many crept into dark corners, hiding behind bedsteads as if they were sandbags. Others sank into such a deep sleep that they had to be forcibly wakened for their meals or for

* Pasewalk.

94

the relief of their natural functions. They were in a semiconscious state, a brutishness, a stupor, retaining only the vegetative aspects of human beings. Their souls were dead so that they did not even complain or cry. Others could not bear the shame and cried like children, desperate, seeking to take their own lives. And more than one succeeded once the end of the war was in sight.

A large part of our efforts — that is, the effort of the doctors, of the officers in charge of the hospital and of the overworked nursing staff — was devoted to saving the patients from themselves, not only each one from himself but also groups from each other. The cursed men often had not experienced enough of the war; they continued it in the hospital, attacked each other with inhuman brutality after they had inflamed themselves with taunts thrown at each other, usually political in nature.

I could not be concerned with each patient in my section. For most of them I made a few notes which I wanted to use later in a scientific work about war psychoses. I attempted to study only a few, to understand the emotional foundation in order to treat or to heal them; among these was an emaciated blind man, highly excitable from sleeplessness, a corporal of the Bavarian regiment, an orderly in the regimental staff — A.H.

I had my attention called to him from two directions. One was an NCO, a former locomotive engineer from Essen, who was responsible for the ward where A.H. was assigned, to keep it in military order and discipline. Another NCO was responsible for treating the patients in this ward, for distributing medicines which were very short in supply, for applying dressings — for more than one had bodily wounds as well as emotional. Both pointed out A.H. as a continual disturber of the peace, a fanatical agitator, a ringleader, a grumbler. He had had to be disciplined several times.

Corporal A.H. indicated that he had been gassed by a grenade which the English had shot off during his last patrol; his eyes had burned like glowing coals; he had staggered back to the regimental staff with his report and had immediately been taken back of the lines. However, he was not in one of the field hospitals with others who had been gassed, whose eyes had been seriously damaged by poison gas, mustard gas and chlorine gas, but he was among the emotionally disturbed. The corporal refused to let the medical

NCO examine his eyes because he had discovered from the loco-motive engineer that the NCO was a Jew. He had a bitter hatred of Jews — it was so strong that he refused to eat at a table with Jews. He avoided them, and maintained that he recognized them by smell.

He did not sleep. At night he wandered in his feverish unrest through the corridors or tossed restlessly on his cot. The others in the ward had to be quiet. They could not smoke, for he was a non-smoker and could not tolerate smoke. They could not drink, for the smell of the bad brandy made him ill. He was an abstainer. Sometimes in the middle of the night he had the desire to order a few friends (there were some who clung to him with fanatical loyalty) to join him by his bed; in spite of his low rank he controlled them. There he would hold unending sermons about his political convictions with such fervor that they could no more sleep afterward than he.

That the others had the same right to sleep and rest as he insisted on having for himself never entered his mind. That they even had rights when something did not suit him seemed to him a personal affront and made him furious.

He had a few simple, clear-cut ideas and was so possessed by them that his circle of adherents steadily increased and the friends of peace in his ward decreased in proportion. He, the blind one, always had a map before him in spirit, and created or destroyed kingdoms with a single word.

The German Fatherland party, a last attempt at the reawakening of the enthusiasm of 1914, had been founded in 1917. It was supposed to be the only patriotic, genuinely nationalistic party, as indicated even in its name. No social classes, no other parties were to be permitted anymore. There was only one great people on earth, the Germans, who had been rightfully chosen by God so that the world might be saved. The king was to the nations of the world as Christ to his apostles, the popular Messiah of the coming generation, the ruling people thanks to their birth, thanks to the spirit of their culture, but, even more, thanks to the invincible German sword and its might. The German sword would unite as a first step all German-speaking, pure-bred peoples of Europe under the banner of an all-encompassing Germany, and then this united kingdom of a hundred million people would rule Europe and thus the entire world. Such a grandiose idea might have been acceptable in 1914, when the army had its first mighty victories. But in 1918, as the retreat on the Western Front was uninterrupted, as tens of thousands of people, especially children, women and old men, died in the hinterlands from hunger, cold and deprivation, it was absurd. But this absurdity, the marvel of it, gained believers for the idea. Out of a political movement a religion developed. That was according to the program of the blind corporal. But in contrast to this divine mission of the Germans, he preached hate of the originator of the war (which he had just praised as the only way to power), the Jew — *der Judt,* as he called him in his Austrian dialect. He did not tolerate argument; his emotions swelled very rapidly to explosive power. He howled, groaned, whispered, and fluted as in a delirium, and often he screamed so loud that the patients in adjacent wards were awakened in spite of their sedatives. *Der Judt* was to blame for everything. He said that these black parasites seduced according to plan the native blond girls and, in doing so, destroyed something that could never be rectified in this world: "Hundreds of thousands of girls are led astray by bow-legged, repulsive Jewish bankers." But that was not enough. Walther Rathenau, the mightiest man in the empire except for the very top generals,* was for him only a diabolical representative of Jewish capitalism which had vowed destruction for Germany. Rathenau was not the great, objective, successful organizer of the German war economy, without whom the war would have been lost by Christmas 1914. No, the war had been lost because this Jewish pig had betrayed and sold, for the sake of the success of the Jewish world conspiracy, the empire which had trusted him. Jews were sowing in the hinterlands and even at the front the dangerous, destructive poison of revolution which the stupid Aryan masses accepted unquestioningly. A.H. insisted that *der Judt* did not work; he supported himself with deceptive usury, he recognized no law, he did nothing but lie, deceive, swindle.

A.H. could be presented with all kinds of contrary evidence, but

* Walther von Rathenau was Minister for Reconstruction and also for International Affairs.

it was all in vain. He was really a man with a quick mentality; he was intelligent, but when he lied, he believed that he was telling the truth. He captured others by means of his idealism; he moved them with his simplicity, and many followed him without question. They did not want to think, to doubt again. Even if a few reminded him that in spite of his claims to great bravery and his marvelous adventures he had achieved only a corporal's rank (he maintained that he had once captured twelve or twenty-five Frenchmen in a cellar in a forsaken spot on the Somme when he was on a solitary patrol), others accepted him as a hero who had been unjustly mistreated, a sacrifice to despotism and injustice. He had made himself beloved in his shabby uniform blouse, his sweaty old green cap cocked at an angle on his head.

He terrorized others as if there were no one else but himself, made demands, insisted that someone always be at his command to help him in his blindness, to dress him, to feed him, to take him on walks, and to help him into the lavatory. But we had hardly enough nursing personnel for those who were violent. The majority had their revenge on him; they plagued him, they questioned his right to the Iron Cross, First Class. He was supposed to have filled in with ink the space in II so that it appeared as I in his records. It is true that personal records were kept very sketchily. He was unbearable, and everyone longed for peace. He was pushed out of bed when he refused to be quiet at night. Saccharine was put in his soup instead of salt; he was led astray, for instance, into the foyer of the officers' mess instead of the lavatory. After all, he was blind, or at least he claimed to be so. The two NCOs got into arguments about him. The best course would have been to remove him from the environment of the emotionally disturbed and to put him in another hospital where he could have awaited the future in the company of patients who were physically ill but emotionally sound. To heal him? How was that possible?

According to my former point of view, the emotionally disturbed who cannot be permanently healed should be protected from society, but even more, society should be protected from them. At P. he was exclusively among people who had lost their emotional balance. Even I was in that condition, and I had to experience much before I again became the person I had been before the war.

And what were the prospects of protecting society from him? Was he not dangerous? "Without scruples, brutal" — these words occurred in his case history again and again. I have treated more than one patient of this kind without ever changing one of them basically. For in the final analysis their changeableness, their untruthfulness, their insatiability, their ignorance of themselves, their inability to commit themselves to another person, yes, even to comprehend only the minimal rights of another person, their ingratitude, their egocentric passion, their hunger for tenderness and for acclaim — all this only a God could have fundamentally changed. However, we were still prone to think of ourselves as kings — like God.

I thought about the miracle of the Kaiser-Jew at my bedside as the broken ribs had penetrated my chest cavity. I thought that I could free the corporal from the most noticeable sufferings of his sickness — the blindness, the insomnia. He was entirely alone. He had never received a package, never a letter from family, father, mother, brother, sister, wife, or fiancée. He had no real friend. During the day he sat hunched in a corner, grumpy, silent, with closed eyes, his long, twisted, Polish mustache above his lips. His opponents went by him and said, "'See how he is spinning." But he spun no bright threads of fate, only black ones. No one had ever seen him laugh; humor was as foreign to him as courtesy. Except for his two or three ideas, he was blind to the world. The only thing that interested him was politics. He persuaded one of his comrades to read the newspapers to him; he could not get enough of that. He grasped matters quickly and surely. He recognized the essential with an intuitive stroke. Kaiser, empire, tradition, boundaries — nothing impressed him.

At that time there were still some comic papers, with sad and puny as well as grotesque and horrible jokes — anything in order to live through this dreary, hopeless period. He refused these vigorously, so that his comrade got tired of always reading only political news, basically the same thing in papers with nationalist, socialist, or democratic leanings. But the corporal insisted. He listened to the articles of the liberal publications with ill-concealed wrath. In some the enemy was granted justice; they dared to doubt that Germany had been forced into the war against its will, an idea which up to that time had been accepted as an indubitable fact. He took the paper and tore it into shreds. He did not want to release the fragments but to dispose of them privately. The other patients in the ward had been waiting for the paper; a new fight broke out in which the corporal was the loser. An artilleryman of Jewish extraction came up to him, his heavy boots clumping and spurs clicking, lifted him by the shoulders, looked into the eyes with which A.H. presumably saw nothing, took his head in both hands, and warned him that if he ever again made a stink he would beat his head against the wall so that he would never forget it. Then he grabbed the paper shreds out of A.H.'s fists and left. He did not hit the blind man — so A.H. spoke scornfully about it. He would have behaved differently in those circumstances. His motto was: God helps those who help themselves. Everything is permitted to the stronger. Even the slightest respect is too much for an opponent.

That same evening he told his comrades planted around the edge of his bed that he had never been able to understand that captured French officers received the same honor as German officers, for example, French pilots who were shot down. The French should not be buried when they died, but the Jews should not even have the honor of fighting in German uniform; they ought to wear yellow identification bands, and so forth.

As an objective doctor I never bothered about all that. He was repulsive, but it was his right to be so. It was not for me to decide either for or against him; I was not to judge.

I had the choice of either ignoring the fanatic or of helping to free him from his miseries by using all the means at hand so that in time the great energy of this man might be used for other, more humane, better goals. I had never acknowledged that a person can be so self-hypnotized that he never learns, never doubts, never grows. But A.H. was one of these.

He did, however, understand how to handle people; he adjusted; he saw us although he did not see us. He knew how to approach the important people, like me, the doctor with the rank of captain who had fought at the front and had won the Iron Cross. He managed it, I do not know how, so that I was especially concerned about him.

One night when I too was troubled with insomnia (I was worried about my mother, who suffered greatly because of all the restrictions), I went to my office and called A.H. to me; he had been wandering around in the corridor like a somnabulist. I put him in the light and kept myself in darkness, far enough removed from the lamp so that I could make my notes unobtrusively. I let him talk, and he spoke for hours without interruption. I discovered that he came from Upper Austria. Because of his love for Germany he had refused to serve in the Austrian army — "I did not want to fight for a Hapsburg" — and had entered the service of the Germans. He had welcomed the war with jubilation as his salvation, as the salvation of the world. His father was a peasant, a little landlord; later he spoke of him as an imperial customs official, a cold, formal, stern man. His father had been married several times; he had children from three marriages, almost like my father. He had lost his mother early; I thought of mine, from whom no good reports came.

He had been a poor student of art in Vienna; he had painted little pictures in oil in a postcard format and then baked them in an oven until they were nicely browned. But he could not gain acceptance to the academy; he had been considered an amateur who would be out of place in a painting class. Out of necessity he had worked as a painter in new construction but had been scorned and driven away without cause by the organized workers who were under the domination of the Jews; all this had happened because the proletarians hated a better person, who was educated, a nonsmoker, a vegetarian, an abstainer. He had wandered around in the streets. Sometimes a goodhearted fellow vagabond gave him a few kreuzers or a fourth of a loaf of bread. There were many of these homeless vagrants who lived at night in deserted channels of the Vienna river under the earth. A.H. had certainly had a much more difficult youth than I.

He had often spent the night in a men's hostel in the Twentieth District, had often wanted to run away from there during the night because the smell of the vagabonds was unbearable to him, but his clothes were gone, being disinfected. He could not get them again until the next morning, all crumpled up and ugly because of the hot disinfectant steam.

He had always been interested in politics; he came from the

101

borderland, where he had seen Germany close at hand and had always longed to be a German because the new Germany of 1870–1871 was strong and hard, the old Austria of 1866, soft and rotten. *Der Judt* had poisoned it, no one else, just as he had poisoned Galicia and devoured it. Again and again he came back to the Jews. They were the black race in the true sense of the word, the mortal enemies of the Germans, the white race — Christians against Jews. Christ had been an Aryan, Judas was the prototype of *der Judt*. The one must live, the other must be destroyed.

I wanted to divert him, in order to lead him to another matter which might be resting in his subconscious. I asked him if he had not been disillusioned by women, if he perhaps had learned to know a Jewish woman who had not been good to him. At first he became fiery red, then pale with anger. But he controlled himself because he wanted to stay on good terms with me. He said spitefully, "The doctor knows everything in any case." And with that the conversation was cut off. He said nothing more, and his empty eyes, gleaming like porcelain, wandered to and fro distractedly. He saw nothing.

He had a coarse, unpleasant voice, but it was difficult to withdraw from it. I had much work scheduled for the next day, but nonetheless I could have listened to him much longer. He was also very fond of good music and most of all loved Wagner, the enemy of the Jew.

The lot of a person struck by hysterical blindness is always very difficult. He is more crippled than one who hobbles along on false legs. He is more unfortunate than a genuinely blind person. The latter often adjusts very quickly to his misfortune. Genuinely blind people look inward. They like to work, are employable, modest, learn to practice a trade, learn to read Braille. Often they establish a family, and their contented facial expressions are astonishing. We sympathize with them, which they do not want, and we try to help them. But it is different with the hysterically blind. Here in the hospital A.H. had no problems. He was there because of the state and was cared for at the expense of the state; he suffered no physical lack. In fact, he had much company, he was provided with all necessities. But the war was coming unquestionably to an end.

What would then happen to this man? Who would assume responsibility for him? No institution for the blind, no regional institution, not even an insane asylum. He had not advanced very far, for the NCO does not begin until the rank of sergeant; he had been a good soldier, the corporal. He was a soldier — nothing else.

But even if the old army continued, what would it do with a man who could not see? He who had begged in the past, who had been reduced to selling postcards from door to door, could continue to beg, but he was not in a position to paint anymore.

Was there any help for him? I thought about it for a long time and finally an idea came to me. I could attempt to find a way to free him from his symptoms through an ingenious coupling of his two ailments with his drive for status, his drive to be like God, his excessive energy. I did not acknowledge to myself that I could not by this means heal his basic illness. In that respect I was blind. I did not want to see it because a kind of passion had seized me. I too wanted to do, to act. I wanted to rule, and every act is more or less a ruling, a change, an elevation of one's self above fate. A.H. too had lifted himself above fate. He preferred to be blind rather than to see the overthrow of Germany. His blindness was a sign of his extraordinarily strong will.

I had to understand this man through my imagination. In spite of his sober drinking habits, he was an incorrigible fantasizer in his delusions of grandeur. I had to approach this man not with logical premises but with a tremendous lie in order to conquer him; for he lied, probably not in the single detail with deliberate purpose, but in his being, for he was really one gigantic lie for whom there was no absolute truth but only the truth of his imagination, his striving, his urges.

I let him know through the friendly NCO that I was interested in his case, which was out of the ordinary and which could perhaps be healed in an hour, and that I would send for him in the course of the day as soon as I had a free minute. It was reported to me that he assumed a derogatory pose; perhaps he was afraid that I had seen through him. I did not send for him immediately. In fact, I had plenty of other work. And I wanted him to be in suspense. He should call on me, he should wait for me expectantly, and he was, as he came tapping down the deserted corridor that evening and desired admittance. I let him come in, continuing to write quietly; he must have heard the scratching of my pen. He did not venture to address me. I let him stand and went out of the room. It was much later when he returned to the corridor.

I took my time. I knew that he did not sleep at all now. The prospect of being able to sleep again excited him so that he could no longer sleep even two or three hours, as he had before. Finally I decided that he was ready. I had him enter, lighted two candles, and began to examine his eyes with an ophthalmoscope. The cornea reflected: it was smooth. The conjunctiva was somewhat inflamed, the result of insomnia. His eyes were somewhat protuberant, blue-gray with a remarkable, piercing, attractive expression; they were wet with tears. A terrible tension was apparent in his features. I saw that he was afraid that I would tell him what all the doctors and the Jewish medical aide had said — that he lied, that his eyes were healthy, and that he could see if he wanted to.

I did the opposite. Sighing, I put the ophthalmoscope back in its case, extinguished the candles, and spoke to him in the dark. Actually, it was dark only for me; for him it had always been so since his departure or his flight from the front. I told him that my original view, in spite of doubts, had been proven true. His eyes had been badly injured by the chlorine gas; he really could not see. I heard him release his breath. I added that I would never have been able to assume that he, a pure Aryan, a good soldier, a knight of the Iron Cross, First Class, would lie and pretend something that did not exist.

Unfortunately, I continued, this conclusion cut off any possibility that I could help him. It would have been simple for me to free him of his sleeplessness if he could have seen my glance or if he could have concentrated his glance on a shining object. Hypnosis works through the eyes. Blind people cannot be hypnotized, at least I could not do it. Everyone has to accept things as they are; there is nothing to be done about fate. After these few sentences I said nothing. It seemed that he wanted to stand up and go away, but I had already caught him, and he sat down again. He shook his head. He struggled against me, but I had become the stronger since I influenced his subconscious. For he wanted to look again into the depths of his soul, and he wanted me to force him to do so. I felt a tremendous joy in my dominance. I had him in my power. Without commanding him, I thought with all my strength that he should fold his hands in his lap. He did it. He should finger his Iron Cross as though he wanted to take it off. He obeyed. I ordered him to tell me his secret concerning women. I overcame his resistance and he spoke. I ordered him to stretch out his right arm; he hesitated, but then he did that too.

No more words. I knew what I had to know. Everything proceeded silently, spirit against spirit. I saw that he was thirsty. I brought him no water. Why should I? It would have been insane to interrupt the sitting then.

After I had discovered everything, it was time to act. I said, "There are no more miracles." His head sank forward on his chest and he did not answer. "No," I continued, "that is true only for average people. Miracles still take place frequently among those who are chosen. There must be miracles, and there must be people to whom nature is subservient, don't you agree?"

"Whatever you say, Doctor," he answered hoarsely.

"I myself am no charlatan, no wonder-worker," I said. "I am a simple doctor. But perhaps you yourself have the rare power, which occurs only occasionally in a thousand years, to work a miracle. Jesus did it. Mohammed. The saints." He did not answer but stared straight ahead and breathed with difficulty. "I could indicate only the method with which you could see even though your eyes have been burned by the mustard gas. An ordinary person with such a condition would be blind for life. But for a person of particular strength of will and spiritual energy there are no limits, the scientific assumptions are no longer valid for him, and the spirit breaks the barrier — in your case, the thick white layer in the cornea — but perhaps you do not have this power to do miracles."

"How can I know?" he asked. "You as staff doctor must know."

"Do you trust yourself to my will?" I answered. "Then try to open your eyes wide. I will light my candle with a match. Did you see sparks?"

"I don't know," he said; "not a light, but a kind of round white glow."

"That is not enough," I said. "That is insufficient. You have to have a blind faith in yourself, then you will stop being blind. You are young, it would be too bad for you to stay blind. You know that Germany needs people who have energy and a blind self-confidence. Austria is at an end, but not Germany."

"I know that," he said in a changed voice. He stood up and held tightly to the edge of the table, but he was still trembling.

"Do you hear?" I said firmly. "I have here two candles, one to the right, one to the left. You must see. Do you see them?"

"I begin to see," he said; "if only it were possible!"

"Everything is possible for you. God helps those who help themselves. A part of God is to be found in every human being — that is the will, the energy. Take hold of all your power. More! Still more! Yet more! Good. That's enough! What do you see?"

"I see your face, your beard, your hand, your signet ring, your white jacket, the newspaper on the table and the drawings above me."

"Sit down," I said, "rest. You are healed, you have made yourself see."

I stood up and walked around the room. He followed me with his eyes just as a person with normal vision would. He looked at the table and tried to decipher my notes.

"You behaved like a man," I said, "and if you have brought sight to your eyes by means of your will power, I will by means of my power bring some healing twilight to your brain, and you will begin as of today to sleep again. You will do whatever I command you for your well-being. Do you agree?"

"Whatever you order, Doctor. To sleep! If you can accomplish that!"

I said nothing more, but had him stand up again and then bedded him on my examination table. I pushed back the lock of hair falling onto his forehead, stroked his damp, cold forehead, and suggested to him, without a word, looking steadily in his eyes, that he close his eyes and not open them again, even if I tried to force them open, and that he sleep without dreaming until the next morning.

Everything happened as I wanted. I had played fate — God — and had given the blind man his eyesight and the capacity to sleep.

The next day I wrote to Helmut, who served in the War Ministry, asking him to try to find an easy position for Corporal A.H., where such a person could recover.

In that period a proclamation by the Jew Walther Rathenau appeared in the newspapers that called for a massive uprising of the people to protect the boundaries. The proclamation brought no response, for Rathenau had no authority and did not know how to capture the imagination of the masses. The army retreated. Dynasties sank, one after the other, without battle and with no outcry from the thrones — and there was no more order. The earlier rulers were accused of having deceived the people with lies. No one wanted to acknowledge that the war was lost and that the people had demanded these lies and deceits.

After the declaration of the armistice, the soldiers and officers bent all their efforts toward going home. The hospital was quickly emptied. The certainty of protection from bullets cured many of those who had been lame, trembling, blinded and deafened by war that no doctor could have helped. I took a leave. In the hospital there was disorder, trouble. No one was in authority since there were no more highest warlords. I gathered together the case histories of different patients, including my notes on A.H. They could be of use to me if I ever wanted to assemble in a scientific work examples of the results of the most powerful sufferings of a spiritual and a physical nature.

I traveled back to M. and took up quarters in the best room of the Prince Regent of Bavaria Hotel, where I had washed dishes as a student. No one recognized me. The personnel had changed. It consisted of old men and young women. All the young men had gone into the field.

The regent of the state of Bavaria no longer existed. In his place were worker and military councillors. But they did not rule. Since no one knew what was most important and since there was no over-all ideal and political goal, no satisfactory conclusion was reached by endless discussions about power. The official ministry had even less power than the councillors, for from where should they draw authority? Perhaps no one wanted to rule or to lead anymore.

I first tried to locate my parents. Since the railroads transported only troops and since no automobile was available, I took a rattling wagon with a lame, badly undernourished horse and drove to S. without inquiring in advance. I rang the old bell; then I knocked on the door of the cottage after no one had come through the high snow of the garden path. The soft voice of my mother, broken by terrible onslaughts of coughing, answered me. I entered.

The room was filled with unpleasant smoke from the smoldering peat. They evidently had no coal, so great piles of black-gray peat clumps were lying on the stove to dry. My mother embraced me with her thin arms; then she lay down on the sofa near the stove and shivered from fever, although she was wearing a sweater over her old clothes. She was almost unrecognizable. She was a shell, the result of TB and worry, only a shadow of the woman whom I had seen just a year before. She coughed steadily, almost without ceasing. Her black eyes, once so striking, lay deep in their sockets, burning with fever. She spoke much, softly, breathlessly, hurriedly — but she seemed to have thought much about everything in advance.

I wanted to move closer to the sofa on which she was reclining, her cover pulled up to her sharp chin, but she begged me not to come too close for fear of infecting me. My father was at the post-office, inquiring about letters from me. The mail carriers were on strike, did not go on their routes, and did not empty the mailboxes; my father did not know if the letters and a telegram which he had sent me in the last three days (it had taken me that long to get here from P., via M., because of poor railroad connections) had reached me in P. She asked me if I were suffering, if I had eaten, if I had a place to stay. I quieted her. I had saved considerable money, for I had not been able to spend much in P. I offered her money. Perhaps she was the one in need. She took the money quickly and hid it under her bolster.

She told me, faltering now and then as if inhibited by shame, that she was not alone with my father, but that the summer guest had returned, the blond child, the disloyal, cunning creature, the impenitent Lutheran. My father and Heidi had discussed matters, but she knew exactly what the situation was. They wanted to be secretive and give her false hope. My father was out of the house almost all day, but Heidi had refused to call the priest today since he had been there just yesterday. But yesterday she had not felt so near death and so lucid as today. Perhaps she had to wait for me. She felt well just then. I should do her the favor of going immediately to the priest and of not being deterred by either my father or the Lutheran girl.

I saw that she was really conscious in spite of her high fever of 39½ degrees. The satanic soul had no power over her, since her reason was sustained by her Catholic faith in the Great Beyond. She detained me for another moment; she formed her words more with her lips than with her breath — it was apparent that her sharp pain made deep breathing and speaking almost impossible. She whispered that she knew she had done me wrong. I was not responsible for Vroni — even Vroni had not been to blame for the whole disaster — and she had specified in her last will that Vroni and my illegitimate brother and sister should receive something from her estate and that Vroni should get the lovely clothes of previous years which still lay in the trunk. She forgave her, also her husband — but not Heidi. Then she whispered, stroking my hands with her almost weightless fingers and holding them one after the other to her lips and to her breast as if I would cool her lips or diminish the pain in her lungs, that I should have patience with her and stay with her to the end. She did not want the doctor to come anymore; the shots were painful and did not help. Science was an idle delusion; she had known that since the days of the Kaiser-Jew. It did not occur to her that she was maligning me and my profession, too. She had to accept her fate, that is why it was called fate, she said with a heart-rending smile that was supposed to be roguish. Suddenly she returned the money to me, was silent for a while, and then said that she would need it no longer. Probably she had wanted to have control of some money for a long time. But Heidi took care of the household.

She looked around with aimless glances and even with a kind of fear, as if she wanted to locate the exit. Then she regained her control. After the burial I should personally give the parish priest a sum for so many masses to be read in S. and in her home church. She did not know if it was sufficient; everything had become so expensive. But I should not be economical, even if I did not believe in purgatory. She wanted to be buried in M. Everything should be in the greatest simplicity. She did not want to die. She had looked forward to my return, and she had prayed often and well for it. God and the Holy Virgin had heard her, so that I survived the war which had cost so many wonderful young people their lives. A shadow passed by the window.

She was speaking even more hoarsely; I had to watch her lips closely in order to understand her. The peat crackled, flared up; for a moment the room was bright, then it was dim again. She did not want me to light the lamp. I think she did not want to shock me with her miserable, neglected appearance. Her feminine pride was not yet gone. She still had all her jewelry, including the brooch which my father had bought on the occasion of the "little operation." Memory surged up in me, pain filled me, and tears began. She saw it with disapproval and drew back toward the wall. I thought to myself that she would be more comfortable if she put on a nightgown and a flannel jacket instead of a dress and a sweater. She shook her head; that did not suit her. She wanted to stay as she was, and she did not want me to make the unavoidable more difficult with my sorrow.

She wanted to die quietly and piously, that is, joyfully and comforted. "Go now, go," she said, but she did not let go of me; she held me unintentionally very firmly, as she had often done years before. I saw that she had something else on her heart, and since the shadow had reappeared at the window and I did not know if we would be alone again during the evening, I asked her to tell it to me quickly. She brightened up at once and came closer to me, moving herself with effort on the sofa. She nodded that I had guessed her thoughts correctly. "But promise me," she said, "that you will not be upset. And that you will never blame me in your thoughts when things are not easy for you. You do not need to answer immediately, you can tell me tomorrow if you want to commit yourself. No, no," she said after a bad coughing spell, her eyelids fluttering nervously above her burning, deep-set eyes, "maybe there will not be any more time tomorrow. Say yes or no, but do not force yourself. But I would die much more peacefully if . . ." But she did not have the courage to say it. She began to talk about the funeral notice; it should expressly say that she had borne her long and painful illness "with Christian patience." "Will you take care of that?" I nodded with tears in my eyes. Then she wanted to list the people whom we should notify so that they could attend the funeral mass and consecration in the church at M. But I did not let her finish the list, I said to her, "You had better talk about what you really want to, what is most important to you. I will obey you."

"You are still young," she said with a relatively clear voice. "You are young and must live. You will marry. A person cannot exist without marriage, especially now, in this time. I cannot stop *him;* he can do what he wants to. But you should promise me not to marry a Lutheran or a Jewess. It would not be a blessing to you. Your father never did believe in the Holy Trinity; therefore, he estranged you from me and we have been unhappy. You should marry a good wife, a good Catholic, poor or rich, it does not matter — do not pay attention to that. Believe me . . ."

I did not let her struggle to say more; I simply gave her my promise.

My father entered wearing a short hunting jacket, the opossum collar full of snow. Heidi came right behind him. He was happy that I was there and showed me several letters that he had written to me, which had been returned and which the postmaster had given back to him. Heidi began to rearrange my mother's bed; she accepted Heidi's capable service with more gratitude and patience than I had anticipated. She did not speak much anymore, but lay there gasping for breath, coughing; her hands moved restlessly over the covers. I went for the priest. He came about eight o'clock and gave her extreme unction. Outside there was deep snow. With powerful strokes, Heidi shoveled a broad path to the garden gate by the light of a pine torch; there had been no candles in the cottage for a long time.

At midnight we thought it had ended, but it lasted until morning. I lay by the bedside of the sufferer with my forehead on the wooden edge of the bedstead. I would have liked to pray; the liturgy came to mind but I could not say it. And I knew that if I could not do it then, I would never be able to, come what may.

My promise did not disturb me. Marriage and Lutherans were not on my mind. I thought only of other things that I regretted: that I had written my diaries in Greek and in runic symbols years

111

before, causing her pain; that I had kept foolish secrets from her; that I had never quite forgiven her injustice; that I had never loved her enough; that I had lived alone with Kaiser as my father and without my mother. But I still loved her. I had only mediocre talents; nothing tremendous had been given me. It is tremendous, however, to forget an injustice and to respond in a moment with a kiss. It is beyond human power and is nonetheless necessary. I understood then that she had been resentful, that she had always waited for me in the belief that I would overcome myself, that I would accept an injustice and love her more than she loved me.

I heard the sound of her breathing growing softer and softer. I was an eyewitness then too, with tears, sighs, and misery. Toward morning I stood up; everything was over, but I did not allow my father or Heidi to come nearer. I closed her eyes. I arranged her hands, which still bore a little of the sacred oil of the last sacrament from the evening before. She could stay in her black dress, but the wool sweater was not appropriate. I got rid of it as well as the many useless medicines.

PART III

M ANY YEARS BEFORE, my parents had bought a plot in the Forest Cemetery in M. My father, however, was opposed to taking the mortal remains of my mother to M., to be consecrated and buried there. Heidi thought it unnecessary and murmured something about South German sentimentality. I did not answer her, but arranged everything as if I were the one to make the decisions. My mother had never liked the village S. She had often in times past visited the gravesite in M. when she felt bad and she had even told me what flowers she wanted on it. My father yielded to me with some embarrassment and shame.

As a veteran of the war, with my decorations and my rank as staff doctor and as captain, I impressed him, and he acknowledged on the way to M. that he personally had always wanted to accede to all the wishes of the dear departed, but the "very practical" Heidi had given him the idea that the burial plot in M. had gone up in price, like everything else, and that without harming anyone, he could make some money if he buried my mother in the inexpensive cemetery in S. and sold the plot in M. After all, my mother would know nothing of it since she was in heaven.

I rented a room for my father next to mine in the Prince Regent. We left the connecting door open and each of us sat at a table — he in his room, I in mine — to write the many funeral notices and telegrams to both the closer and the distant acquaintances. My father wept copiously. I could not do that. I could weep only occasionally.

Perhaps I had not yet comprehended how great my loss was. The corpse had been brought in a closed wagon to M. and laid out there. As my father and I stood in front of the resplendent church across from which I had lived as a young student, I thought of my great longing for her and the tenderness which had overwhelmed me at that time in my need as a hunger-stricken student, how I had pressed the hot grog glass against my cheek, thinking of her, and how, standing at the window, I had shown her photograph the Alpine landscape and the tower of the church, in the interior of which now her catafalque stood, covered with silver decorations and crosses.

Unexpectedly the tears came. I knelt at her coffin, my father next to me. In the meantime the church had filled with many people, and autos and carriages kept arriving.

At the end of the mass, we went at the head of a rather long funeral procession quietly and reverently out of the church, and a great many horse-drawn droshkies went to the cemetery in glistening, dry, snowy weather. There the body was once more consecrated and a short prayer uttered; then a gravedigger approached my father, who could see nothing because of his tears, and pressed a shiny trowel into his hand so that he could pour some earth into the grave, into which the black-lacquered coffin had been lowered by means of creaking ropes.

I saw everything clearly and with a firm hand poured a chunk of hard earth, frozen like a stone, into the grave.

Then we had the most unpleasant part before us — thanking all the guests and shaking their hands. I did not know if I should take off my black gloves or not. My father kept his on; it was cold and he had always had very tender hands. He smiled sadly and modestly, but he was honored, pleased, and comforted that many of his friends from his best years had remembered him when they saw the death notice in the daily paper and had come — the director and his wife, both in beautiful furs, the owner of the house in which I had spent my childhood, the lawyer who had defended my father, his friends from his favorite restaurant. Many of my acquaintances had come too. Councillor von Kaiser, still unbent, with his strangely weathered face, his fiery eyes under the bushy snow-white brows. His son Helmut, who smiled at me warmly and intimately and whom I softly asked to visit me soon, was in uniform as I was. Even the old Kaiser-Jew appeared; he was one of the few who wept. With his good, loyal heart he had forgotten everything that had occurred between them and remembered only that she had been in his care for years and that he had wanted to help all of us. Even his daughter was there, lovelier than ever. In spite of the sad time, a thrill of pleasure went through my heart as she shook my hand and looked at me with her large, clear, blue-green eyes, which held my glance. But unlike her father, she had not forgotten everything. Something bitter and domineering remained, and I saw that she did not let the earth slide gently from her trowel onto the coffin but flung it down with force.

Our summer guest, the blond Heidi, had not been at the mass in the church; perhaps as a Protestant she did not appreciate such ceremonies. At the cemetery she was present; she stayed close to my father, without being conspicuous, dressed in simple dark clothes, and her nearness seemed to help him. She did not throw any earth onto the coffin. Besides these visitors on whom we had more or less counted, four others had come who were quite unexpected. Vroni, looking worn out but still with a kind of austere peasant beauty in her features and bearing, was there with her two children, now thirteen years old, who had inherited her beauty, which was in their case still tender and soft, and who resembled my father — and me. They were all poorly dressed. I noticed that her hair which had been coal black and her skin which had been fresh and blooming bore brassy yellow spots like those developed by munitions plant employees who had to fill the explosives containing nitroglycerine. So the evidences of war were present in her too.

If the appearance of these people was an unpleasant surprise for my father and his Heidi, the reappearance of Angelica, the former housekeeper of Councillor von Kaiser, was so for me, for I had never expected to see her again. She had come, however, dressed very properly in a well-tailored and beautifully fitting mourning dress. Her husband, a major, had fallen on the field of honor during the retreat on the Western Front, she told me, and I had to console her as she did me. She held my hand longer than necessary. And I must say that as much as the beautiful, proud, implacable Victoria had pleased me, I was glad that the aging, humble Angelica did not want to let go of my hand and that she begged me with a beseeching glance to forget the past. What did I have to forgive her? We had lived together for years and then we had gone our own way for years. There was nothing to forgive.

In the meantime God's acre (as my mother had always called this cemetery) had emptied. The sun set, blood-red, over the clear, silver-gray and snow-covered mountains. A bitter cold breeze came from the nearby river in which the ice crashed as it moved. We went silently back home through the dimly lighted streets. In front of the grocery stores were the long silent queues, as they had been for the previous three years. The cannons were quiet, the flame-throwers had been quenched, the gas grenades no longer burst, and the planes were silent; the heavens had again become the heavens with clouds, stars, and blue — but there was no peace. The war was over, but the blockade continued. Hunger, cold, privation. No bread arrived.

When we got home to S. in the evening we were grateful that the practical Heidi had found some food. It was black market, that is, it was a secretly slaughtered suckling pig. She had even managed to find a few pieces of coal and some decent wood for the big stove in the living room. Perhaps I should not have sat down at that table or warmed myself at that stove — but I did nevertheless. In the course of the evening I left for an hour so that Heidi and my father could discuss their affairs. I went to the parish priest to give him the money for the masses as my mother had wanted. He kept me somewhat longer than I had anticipated.

I found the priest to be a good-spirited man, not a fanatic, who had, however, been overwhelmed by the unusually difficult times. He had to struggle to remember my mother, although he had seen her every Sunday in his church through the years and had administered the last rites to her. He made a note of the sum I gave him in a thick book and marked the date on the calendar for the first of the memorial masses. He did not let me go before he had offered me a glass of brandy which the farmers around S. secretly brewed and which I would have liked best to spit out at once, for alcohol, even in small quantities, had not been good for me, probably since the attacks on the Gurkhas.

He noticed my embarrassment, had me sit down again, and began talking about the immorality of the peasants, or better of their wives, who lived in heathen fashion with the sturdy Russian prisoners who worked with them in the summer in the fields and in the winter sat with them by the hearths; they bore innumerable children about whom only one thing could be said for sure — their father was not a Catholic Christian from the neighborhood. "And how will it be now when we no longer have a king and all governing bodies and courts are being scrapped?"

I comforted him, for I believed that the chaos would last only until the conclusion of the peace, which seemed to be nearer, thanks to the tractability of the German military staff and the longing for peace among the people.

He asked about my experiences in the war. I answered only that I had been a doctor in the field. I said nothing about the storm troops. And yet the short time as a storm trooper had affected me much more deeply than the long time with amputations, not to mention with the spiritual wrecks of war in P. He thought that a young capable Catholic doctor would have a real opportunity in his area. He had great concern for his parish; I saw that I had been badly mistaken when I had considered him somewhat backward. He told me that the former doctor had died from typhus in 1916; he had been much loved. He was staff doctor in the Carpathians with the Bavarian Southern Army at the time of his death. The young doctors who had worked in S. as substitutes had been drafted one after the other, and the last one had been so ill prepared because of irregular studies that not long before a woodcutter's wife near Schrangen had died in childbirth. The child, unbaptized, had died with her while the young doctor had sat there and rumpled his hair. Would I be interested in settling in S.? I said that I would think about it, and I returned to my father and Heidi.

In the short time since the death of my poor mother, they had changed the whole house to their fancy. Much had become better, I will grant, for they were people who wanted to enjoy life and who were not concerned about otherworldly matters. They wanted everything as pleasant as possible and were serious only about their own well-being. They were healthy and vigorous. I held myself aloof; the picture of my mother appeared more and more often to me, and at night my lips moved, and I talked with her, almost all night, but quietly so that neither Heidi nor my father in the next room could hear me.

Then I sank into a quiet sleep. But my dream was in no way quiet. It took me into the middle of an attack on the Gurkhas and was connected in a senseless but suggestive way with my memories of the amputations. I wanted to forget this dream, but it stayed with me throughout the day. So I too was still in the war, and there was no peace as yet.

I decided to take a course in the obstetrical clinic of M., since I had discovered from the stories of the priest that a rural doctor in such a mountain area had a great responsibility and needed to be well prepared in order to be able to deliver babies successfully even in a poverty-stricken woodcutter's hut without light and with no resources.

The general distress, instead of diminishing, grew more and more. Births were rather easy. No forceps were necessary, rarely even a shift in position, never a Caesarean, for the miserable "fruits" of the women after four years of war were so thin, so pliable, that the births proceeded easily. Even the loss of blood of the half-starved mothers was minimal. If, however, there was a hemorrhage, the poor things were lost, for how could the blood be replaced? They also had the greatest difficulty in nursing the infants, and many despaired. I used all my powers and suggestions to give them some hope for a better future.

Finally in the summer of 1918 the frightful peace treaty of Versailles was signed, crushing all my hopes to nothing.

At that time I often felt driven to the church. When the organ resounded, when suddenly in the icy stillness of the transubstantiation the little bell rang softly but penetrated everything, a powerful shudder went through me. I sank into a transport which drove me upward through the Gothic arches, my cheeks burned, my heart pounded, I dropped to my knees like the others, obedient and humble. I prayed even though I did not believe.

Often, too, I was drawn to crowds, which I had always avoided before. The Catholic processions in which my mother had once found comfort and forgetfulness of her suffering no longer took place, but every day in the city there were great demonstrations, particularly in the factory areas. People — pale, in torn clothes, with stern, starved, care-worn faces, their fists clenched in the pockets of their loose coats, many in uniform with no rank insignia — marched, shouting steadily their cries as if out of one mouth, their oaths and curses, the names of their political leaders or other slogans. I spent the mornings in the clinic as a clear, observant, responsible clinical doctor, an individual; in the afternoons I was absorbed in the mass which drew me irresistibly along. And I forgot myself, the period and its distress. I have to admit that I forgot it more easily when I marched in step than I did in church.

❉

The need became more and more desperate. If one had believed that it could not get worse, it still did, and there was no end in sight.

Wars have been common since the beginning of history. Our modest dynasty was not the first which had fallen because of a modest revolution. But what was unknown was the overall hunger which the helpless authorities, struggling for their existence, could not alleviate — their impotence, the absence of safety in the streets, the lack of coal, clothing, all necessities, and finally the devaluation of the money. Money was no longer sacred after neither the king nor the church was sacred anymore. No one could escape from this loss, this marshy, sinking disappearance of money. Rich was rich no more, for everyone got poorer by the day — except for a few scoundrels who kept their secrets hidden. It was as if a ship which had battled wind and weather for a long time and believed itself to be safe was stranded because under its keel the sea disappeared into nothingness. The ocean waters which had borne the ship fled away in all directions. Never was the proverb "We are on dry land" more merciless and more true. Loyalty and faith disappeared. What had been bought or sold one day for a hundred marks was worth more or less the next. No contract, no rate of exchange was valid; one doubted everything after one had begun to doubt stable prices which a loaf of wartime bread, a night in a hotel, a piece of clothing made of synthetic stuff with a certificate of need cost — or what a book, a visit to the doctor, a piece of soap, a stamp might cost.

I had two homes: one in T., where I wanted to set up my practice as a country doctor, and a second in the Prince Regent. I saw everything from the point of view of both the metropolis and the country.

Clothing was a real problem. I had had my old uniforms somewhat remodeled; I had taken off the epaulettes and other insignia of rank. In the city I wore these military-looking suits and the long officer's coat which went with them. For the country I had received a few pieces of clothing from my father that were still wearable. He bought new clothes, probably to please Heidi, whom he wanted to impress as an elegant, vigorous and well-dressed man. My prewar clothing I had generously and stupidly given away when I went into service. Who would have thought that I would return to a period in which not a single genuine thread was to be had. My father would not have been able to get a new shirt for his wedding if he had not begun already, in the second year of the war, to hoard all kinds of good things — linen, materials, foreign currency and everything imaginable, including lard in stone jars.

Sometimes I had a free hour. I would telephone Victoria. She did not have to be begged but came. We met — sometimes here, sometimes there, almost always in the presence of a third person. She remained cool, which I had expected. But she grew more and more so, which hurt me. I did not know what she wanted. She understood me very well in my despair about myself and the time, but she did not comfort me. Did she still love her deceased husband? Her old father showed more warmth and kindness to me in a minute than she did over several months.

I remembered my mother and my promise to her on her deathbed. I did not want to love — I wanted to remain free. I did not want to marry a Jewess. But I was in love for the first time. I had to. I did not ask anymore if the "vessel" were pure or impure. I had given my mother my word on her deathbed. My mother was dead. Victoria lived and was beautiful, all the more beautiful the colder she was. I would have liked to kiss her lips, but they were hard, ironic, imperious, and gave neither a caress nor a kind word.

It was a lot when she admitted to me once with her pale face turned away that she had nothing against me; on the contrary, but she could not forget her husband who had fallen in the war. The day before she had burned drafts of his speeches and had thought of me while she shed angry tears. He had loved his people — the Germans, not the Jews — more than her. But was that the real reason? I doubted it.

My father advised me to help him in his small wood factory. He had changed over to making furniture. He remained modest, he smiled at me, and he was on a more secure base than many others. He had a large quantity of good wood in his sheds, and he was one of the first to insist on payments in foreign currency or on the basis of a definite code. Since he manufactured stuff which was sought for, he could stick to his demands. Ever since he had had the trouble with the poor material in the bridge, he bragged about his good, solid materials, well-dried wood and so on.

He had formed a local group of the Democratic party in S., composed of veterans as well as some very young men and women. I was asked to join. In fact, they anticipated great things from me, since as a former officer and a doctor I was highly respected and had a certain quiet power. It was said that I could speak and persuade, and I finally began to believe it, although I was always only a mediocre, controlled orator.

I was not perturbed by the presence of a large crowd, but neither did it inspire me. I recognized that I ought to cooperate, for the program was humane and politically sensible. It preached freedom — that is, adjustment between the will of the individual to dominate and the interests of the masses. It demanded quiet patience and insight into the mistakes made during the war years. It set clear and moderate goals in contrast to the aimlessness of the Fatherland party, which had been dissolved right after the national collapse but whose spirit was still very much alive. But to my shame, I have to confess that the thought of Victoria let me say no, for they wanted to choose me out of the mass of members for a responsible position and nominate me as a candidate to the assembly. I thought I would gain in her opinion if I sacrificed myself politically, for she did not want a politician as a husband. But it made no impression on her. If she had been cool before, then she was icy.

I could not live without her, that is, without hope of winning her, and how could I have hope if I never saw her? Therefore I decided not to meet her anymore and stayed away without an explanation. I tried to conquer my feelings by means of my will power.

At that time I drew closer to my boyhood friend Helmut. He was assigned to the Bavarian General Staff — I do not know whether it was because of his particular military capacities or because of his relationship with Captain R.,* who at that time was the spiritual leader of the General Staff in Bavaria.

The Hungarian and Bavarian Soviet Republics had collapsed, and the battle against the moderate, weak, tottering German republic, called the Weimar Republic, began. R., who was an impossibly

* Ernst Röhm was chief commander of the SA, or the "storm troopers."

ugly man, devoted to homosexuality, without scruples, brutal with a powerful strength of will and unusually clear insight, certainly did not see his equal in little Helmut. He confided in him as a man in an important position might confide in his "Benjamin," and Helmut kept no secrets from me.

R. made no secret of his stand. He had sworn loyalty as an officer to Weimar and to the president; like Helmut he accepted a generous salary from the all-too-trusting republic, but he opposed it very openly. "I am not willing," he said when asked, "to give up my right to political thinking and acting in the framework of the activity assigned to me. I will make use of it." But what was the corps of officers striving for? The return — yes, the outstripping — of the circumstances of 1914, the rule of the sword, the militarization of the nation and a war of revenge.

The goals were simple and brutal; the methods, however, were devious and cunning. On the insistence of the officers' corps, which was the single support for Weimar since the working class was split into a conservative, a liberal, a bourgeois, and a revolutionary, proletarian, international wing, the troops were denied the vote. The republican, the revolutionary parties, the so-called November parties, were forbidden to seek members in the army. November, the great revolution without bloodshed,* was considered in these circles as a humiliation, as a desertion to the enemy, as a dagger thrust in the back of the undefeated army.

The leaders could then mold like wax their subordinates as a model army in the new structure and infect them with their ideals, their goals, their methods. For them the war was not at an end. I, too, felt that things could not remain as they were.

Helmut and R. were grateful that I had called to their attention in the fall of 1918 the war-blinded A.H., the miraculously healed fanatic, this man seemingly so simple but endowed with mysterious powers. They had discovered his power, and he possessed something which they needed.

The military units in M. had at that time begun investigations that would determine which of their members had been involved in revolutionary acts, in the November disgrace and in the Soviet re-

* The November Revolution in 1918 followed the defeat of Germany.

public. Corporal A.H. had been put in charge of one such investigative commission. He had stood the test. He condemned everyone who came before him, without exception, probably also without differentiation and without justice.

But in that only his fanaticism was apparent, not his sinister powers. These were discovered soon afterward. They had him take part in a course in which the soldiers were to be politically educated. He was to counteract the socialist and republican poison with speeches. He proved his dependability. He was on the right side, on the side of those in power.

The General Staff sought to educate agitators, at first for propaganda in the narrowest circle. The political courses of the Bavarian Army did not consist of boring hours of dictation, but of lectures with heated discussions. One day the opportunity came for the corporal to enter the discussion.

It concerned the Jews. A few speakers were not very much in favor of them, others not very much opposed. But then came A.H. With senseless anger he threw himself into the discussion and talked himself, as he had often done in P., into an intoxicated delirium, which no one could withstand. He beat and thrashed down his opponents, left no opportunity for counterarguments; he accepted no logic, no historical fact. He never granted his opponents even a fractional concession; the longer he spoke, the more fanatical he became. He was insatiable, unrestrained, demonic; he hypnotized those present, as I had once hypnotized him, by the energy of an idea hammered a thousand times by the narrowing of the mental field of vision. No depth of spirit. No doubt. No relearning. No additional learning. One idea, two, at the most three — but these repeated again and again with ever more powerful intensity in the sweat of his face, blind with religious fanaticism, with gestures filled with splendid force, tears in his eyes, beside himself, almost outside the world. Thus I saw him again after several years as I sat between Helmut and R. and listened to his first major speech in the Meadow Barracks.

The auditorium was familiar to me. It was a room for the enlisted men of that barracks which had now been changed to a barracks for the imperial army. It was the same room into which I had been brought after my accident. It was filled to bursting and echoed with wild applause. A.H.'s triumph was great. Captain R. approached the corporal, who immediately stood at attention, and promised to nominate him as an educational officer. Already, in the last part of the war, officers had been sent to the front for the purpose of strengthening morale, and they had been designated as instructional officers.

A.H. recognized me. He grew pale and turned his eyes away. Then he forced himself and gave me his hand. I saw that he had an aversion to me. That gave me a good, warm feeling; I wanted to help him further. Was he not my production?

In those times, which were more difficult than all that had gone before, I was more sensitive to pain than ever. My love for Victoria was one source of constant suffering. I cannot express it even now and do not understand it, how deeply it affected me and how unhappy I was. Loneliness did not help me, and my will power yielded to my emotions. In church, where I was drawn again and again, even though I believed neither in God nor in Christ nor in miracles, I prayed, but the prayers were contradictory. Once I prayed that I could forget Victoria, another time that in spite of everything I could find happiness with her. And although I did not believe in God, I sought him as a power superior to me.

I still had from previous years a fatherly friend, a man of high mental authority who had trained and led me as a student and as a young doctor until the outbreak of the war. Neither I nor numberless others could live in such times entirely without direction. How gladly I would have confided in Councillor von Kaiser. How often I had thought of trying to find him, until accident, or fate, led him to me — had to lead him, for he was in a similar situation to mine. I saw this man — in church. He was on his knees next to me, and in the dimness we did not recognize each other until we both stood up. His weathered features showed neither worship of the heavenly Father nor comfort, nor hope of the salvation of pious Christians in another world and gratitude — only stark desperation. I saw myself reflected.

To be sure, he was a man standing on the doorstep of age, and I was only a little over thirty. It was all the sadder that even I, in the strength of my manhood and with clear understanding and knowledge, could find no resistance to the confusion and despair of a time of upheaval and was not equal to my difficult but not really hopeless love for Victoria.

I went home with von Kaiser. I learned what I had suspected — that he sought comfort in the church, not because his Katinka was far away, but because she had returned to him. To be sure, it was another Katinka, no longer the childish thing with the rosy voice, but an indifferent, elderly child with no illusions, who lived from day to day and sought to become intoxicated every day by some means. She had separated from Oswald Schwarz "in all love and goodness," since he had not been able to renounce his old attraction to men who provided him with mental stimulation as well as tenderness.

Father Kaiser therefore had two people under his roof whom Oswald Schwarz had attracted and then repudiated: Helmut and Katinka. She was satisfied to accept the tenderness of her old lover; in fact, she sought it. She wanted to be loved. He was the only person — she sought to flatter him — who still played a role in her life, as if the lovelorn women whom she attracted and repelled and with whom she played — as Oswald Schwarz had played with her in the end — counted for nothing.

Kaiser knew exactly where he stood. He could have voluntarily separated from Katinka, left her to her own devices, assured her of only her livelihood, which he would have been able to do because of the fortune he had invested well in the Bank of England. But he preferred to live from the scraps which Katinka, now a beggar for love, threw him according to her mood and whim.

But his light was not extinguished. His dark eyes burned with passionate love; the clarity of his spirit was not dimmed. He saw much, maybe nearly everything, clearly. It was he who overcame his prejudice toward the Jews first and recognized the three great accomplishments of the Jew Rathenau. But I upbraided him with just that, for since Oswald Schwarz wanted nothing to do with Katinka, Kaiser had a good feeling about the Jews. He saw in the great Jew Rathenau the savior of the crushed empire: first because of his accomplishment during the war, his organization of the German military economy; then because of his call in November 1918 for a mass uprising; and finally because of his last diplomatic act, that is, the Treaty of Rapallo with the Bolsheviks. This treaty was the first step in the return of Germany to the world political scene.

The all-German program of the Fatherland party was more alive than ever. It had not been negated by the strategic loss of the war. Only the battles had been lost; the ancient ideals had been too vague. But Germany had survived the catastrophe; therefore it had been victorious. That war had been won. Only two conditions had to be fulfilled (both of which Rathenau had accomplished): Germany must have the protection for the rear in the East which Bismarck had demanded — toward Russia with its gigantic supply of minerals, with its huge, unpopulated, easily tillable prairies stretching to East Asia, with its dull human material capable of greatness, which needed German education, German discipline and the German genius for organization. But Rathenau was not considered a statesman in nationalist circles and in the army. The treaty with Russia was popular among the generals, but their hatred of the Jew blinded them to all else. And second, why should Germany not depend on the spirit of cosmopolitanism, on the Jews, who always, in spite of all their weaknesses and although they had occupied only a modest place in the empire, had been numbered among the best German patriots. Kaiser named the Socialist deputy Lazarus, Victoria's husband, who had gone into the war for his fatherland and had fallen, and the example of Ballin, the founder of the German mercantile fleet, who — unlike his patron, the former kaiser, who wanted only to survive the war — had committed suicide out of love for his country, not out of love for his blood. I recognized all that — Kaiser had far-reaching plausible ideas — but nonetheless I did not follow him. He did not sweep me along. He was a human being like me; he loved as I did. His personality no longer overpowered me as Rathenau's personality had not overpowered the German people.

He sought a friend in me. I accepted the friendship. It was better than nothing. But I did not confide my own experiences to him, and when he sought refuge with me because his Katinka quartered her beloved "little mice," her friends in the common household, I could smile sympathetically about his weakness.

Rathenau fell in this period, the victim of the bullets of young fanatics. They had been uprooted and deliberately urged on to their terrible goal by fanatical, false teaching; they had believed that through their horrible murder they would free the fatherland from a Jewish traitor.

Germany remained quiet. No one was upset. People felt sorry for Rathenau, for the poor murderers who, surrounded on all sides, committed suicide in a deserted, ruined fortress. No one looked seriously for the real instigators of the deed, who from what I heard through Helmut and his friend R. could have been found, and the unrestrained patriotism of the two fanatics seemed to many to be a justification. It could have been the moment for a revolution, but it was only an honorable burial for Rathenau.

My father came to me. He told me that he wanted to marry Heidi. Vroni and her children had accepted the bequest from my mother and thereby showed that they would be content with money. He certainly had loved Vroni, but he had to demonstrate his gratitude to Heidi, his honor demanded that. In his false modesty, he acted as if he wanted to reward Heidi with a wedding ring for the services which she had performed for my mother during her long illness. I knew better. I knew that my mother had died by a peat fire and that two days later there was a coal-and-wood fire. But I did not raise objections. Perhaps I could have restrained my father, for he was still uncertain — he knew all three women: my stern mother, Vroni, and Heidi, and as an aging man he feared Heidi's tyranny. Perhaps that was why he came to me, for he certainly did not need my agreement. Vroni would have been his slave.

But something drove me, as with so many young people, to be fair to everyone, and as my mother had expressed it, to carry water on both shoulders. Vroni had struggled to keep herself and my brother and sister during the war years; she had passed up more than one opportunity to marry a workman or a small landowner because . . . Was it my fault? Certainly. No one else but I, by sending her twenty marks a month through the years, had given her the idea that my father still loved her, more than ever, and that he was honestly concerned about her and the two children and would honor an unwritten promise to marry her after the death of my mother. Now my mother was no longer there. My father was free. He had money again; he was healthy and independent; he could do what he wanted. I stood objectively above them all, I thought. On the one side the worn, aging Vroni, with the incurable bitterness about all the good years lost, without education, and as a proletarian essentially averse to us (her glances at the graveside of my mother had spoken very clearly); on the other side Heidi, a teacher from a good home, in full bloom, optimistic, not without money and with good social capacities, a superior housewife. So I let matters take their course, and they ended with my father's marriage to Heidi, to Vroni's great dismay and disillusion. My father did not love me any more than before. Heidi had never trusted me. Vroni hated me because she believed that I had turned my father against her and plotted against the marriage.

I came to another solution and offered it to Vroni and her almost grown children. I needed a housekeeper in my house on the road between S. and T. I would have been glad to take Vroni and the children. I would have tried to train the children and to help them. I wanted to recognize them as my brother and sister, which after all they were. Nothing came of it. Vroni spewed poison and gall as I offered it to her. She had been a servant and a factory worker long enough. She wanted to be my father's wife or nothing else. She deserved that because of her loyalty, and so on. She went so far as to scream that she would throw at our feet the compensation which my mother had willed her in scorn in order to buy off the demands which she had on my father. She was so angry and so abusive in her language that I broke off the conversation, for it was not suitable for the ears of the children, who were present.

I was not old. I needed a wife. I did not love Angelica anymore. Actually, I had never loved her; in fact, I had believed that I was not capable of a deep passion, and we had lived together as two good friends. But I loved Victoria and could not win her even though, in spite of all my efforts, I could not forget her.

Angelica came to me. She cried. She begged me for the sake of my former love and kindness, she threw herself at my feet as if she had to ask pardon for something terrible. I raised her coldly. I spoke kindly to her, as to a patient. Her eyes dried immediately; she sat down comfortably in an armchair and looked around with the eyes of a housewife at the neglected room, full of dust and spider webs. The house was overgrown on the outside with ivy; all

kinds of insects found their way into my consultation room, where I
received my patients.

We did not say anything more about our future, as we had done
in our good times. Angelica was intelligent and had to know that
I did not love her. I should not have taken her in. But I did it anyhow, out of fear of loneliness, and I felt in better spirits when she
had put away her things in the house but not in my room. She
stayed aloof from me.

In the evenings when I returned home, dead tired, I found everything prepared. She had noted during my absence what the patients had told her; I could depend on her messages, discuss my
cases with her. She had not lived uselessly for so many years in
the house of a doctor like von Kaiser. She expected no tenderness,
no kiss; her handshake, even her glance, remained comradely cool.
I thought that I had to be thankful and be just. I took up the
same argument which I had recognized as being hollow when my
father presented it in order to justify his marriage to Heidi. I drew
her one evening into my bedroom; then suddenly I was afraid of
her, of myself. I pushed her away; again she lay at my feet as if
she wanted to be trodden on, but also raised again, seized — I was
only too aware of it. It was not the measured, harmonious tenderness of the prewar time, but I yielded to my dull instincts which I
had recognized in myself after the Gurkha attacks, and she yielded
to her longing for pain, for serving, for slavishness. Before, we had
separated quietly after a nice hour together, each with a cigarette
in our mouth; now the kisses and intoxication lasted almost all
night. In the intervals she pressed herself to me with such force
that my ribs pained me.

She told me in whispers, with heated breathing as of a wonderful
mystery, about A.H., among whose most ardent followers she belonged because he was so pure and presumably had never touched
a woman. She knew that I had known him in the last days of the
war. How much she wanted to know more about him!

In spite of all my overcharged passion I remained estranged from
her, and so I never told her anything about A.H. or about Victoria.
I thought that she suspected nothing. But in spite of her appearance
as an honest soul, loyal to me, "the slave of the noble lord" as she
called herself in sentimental modesty, she knew at least this much —

that she did not know everything. Purposely she avoided speaking of A.H.'s fanatic hatred of the Jews. She saw in him a man free of all hate, filled solely with love, love of the fatherland, whom everyone should value. So she had hardly missed one of his many gatherings, in which he celebrated his triumph as an orator.

One evening she persuaded me to go to M. with her and to leave the care of the telephone to Heidi, with whom she had quickly become friendly. We wanted to telephone from M. to S. to be sure that I had not been called to a patient in the meantime.

It was the third time that I had heard A.H. as an orator. The first time had been at the hospital in P. — one against one. The second time had been in the troop auditorium — he on one side and a thickly jammed crowd of soldiers and officers on the other. That evening I saw him for the first time in a throng — one against three thousand. He stood above the crowd, for he was untouched by it; it impressed him as little as earlier. He despised it. The crowd, on the other hand, was completely enthralled by him.

He had the habit of speaking only in the evening. Then his listeners were tired, unresisting. They wanted to sleep, dream, be carried away, adore, obey blindly, be possessed by the spirit. Hardly anyone was left untouched, for he intoxicated himself. He showed everyone how glorious it was to be possessed of a single, powerful, worldly idea. Even people like me, who had come skeptically and with a medical diagnosis in mind, were enslaved — only momentarily, but nonetheless completely overcome. This was what he wanted — thus his expectations were fulfilled. He wanted this joy. His emotion worked on our emotion.

His instinct, not his book learning, had shown him how an individual gains control over all others, how he speaks from above and the others listen below, lord over servants, a magician, a despot, a wizard, and a terrible, hard priest — all in one.

But was he himself such a strong person that it was pleasurable to such as us, man and woman — me, the eyewitness, the objective, experienced doctor, as well as Angelica, the slave addicted to pain — to feel his fist and to succumb to him? Had he saved himself in the greatest danger and remained a man? Had he, a man like Rathenau, thrown a heroic battle cry as a desperate counter-measure to fate? Had he not really hidden himself from the facts, staggered from the front, crept away, a coward, behind his blindness, his helplessness, until better times had come and the army had freed his tongue, fanned the holy fire in him, taken him under its wing?

Meaningless evaluations of my brain, meaningless resistance of my will!

He spoke; I surrendered. He talked us down, intelligent and foolish, man and woman, old and young. He never came to an end, for a quarter of an hour, for a half-hour, for three, four hours, always the same, never anything else; eternally in a circle he bored until he had reached into the depths. He repeated his message not seven times but seventy-seven, and yet he was not satisfied.

After a quarter of an hour he was dripping wet; his collar stuck to him like a wet rag at his throat, the veins were swollen in his forehead, he shuddered as in a fever, he threatened with widespread gestures, he enticed us, he exorcised us. He had thrown the lock of hair, as in P., over his forehead, and still he did not stop, and no one wanted it to end. Everyone trembled in expectation of something monstrous, and I noticed with a shudder that I trembled like everyone else and that I had become only one atom in the total mass.

I had been warned. Kaiser had told me how things were at one of A.H.'s meetings.

From the beginning of his consciousness of his superpower, A.H. had spurned what other parties, including ours, needed: police protection in the auditorium. He maintained correctly that the masses, who were his only concern, would see that as a sign of weakness. He was the lord, he had the rights of a lord. He was right. He was the law. Anyone who thought differently was of the devil. He boasted of this, just as his Captain R. boasted of his rights with the weak Weimar Republic. "We have sharply emphasized our lordly privileges without ceasing, in every minute. Our opponents know exactly that whoever provokes at any time is thrown out with no leniency." This was his basic principle. The form was banal, the speech ordinary, but there was no one who could misunderstand. "Every attempt at a disturbance will be stifled in the bud. The originators of it will fly down the stairs with broken heads."

Right at the beginning of that meeting I experienced it (without venturing to stir). A skinny little man with a piping voice interrupted the speaker with a thin, shrill cry of "freedom." In less than ten seconds, several powerful, tall men, with that expression in their eyes that my comrades and I had had when we had attacked the Gurkhas, threw themselves at the poor little creature, beat his head to the ground, bloodied his face, picked him up like a feather, and literally threw him down the stairs. Others made a path for them.

The speaker on the podium had not halted; he knew us and his people. They were his bodyguard, a crowd of dangerous, rough fellows, who, as I knew, had often enough broken up other meetings with brutal power — Democratic, Communist, Catholic. They could kill with their fists. Like the heathen, they worshiped their idol, they gambled with their lives, they were his surest protection. He called them his "loyal comrades." The opponents were "bandits." "A determined bandit should have the power to make my political activity impossible for me, a respectable person?" he had once said to R., who had smiled. He listened indulgently to A.H. when he spoke with fanatic hate of "Marxist-Jewish" subhuman beings but acknowledged that he had never read Marx. He said that his blood, the German blood, led him. It could never err. He could never err.

I knew what he was. I had been his eyewitness, his resuscitator. I was the first miracle-worker on this miracle — and yet I surrendered to him. Seventy million people succumbed to this Mohammed without a god; why should I claim to have been stronger than they? I noticed on the faces around me, in the tense, disturbed features, in the trembling limbs of Angelica, that the climax had not yet been reached but that it had to come in the next few seconds. After a monstrous, unfathomable outburst of hate against the Marxist brood of Jews, it came over him and over us. It was the moment when the orator with his hoarse voice, his Austrian accent, suddenly lost himself — German blood! German blood! German blood! he screamed — one did not know whether it was out of love for this blood or out of fear for this divine blood. Did he himself know? He spoke in tongues. It overcame him, it overcame us; and we were no longer what we had been before. Perhaps if I had been alone with him, and if he had had the same ecstasy in the consultation room of P., I would have been able to remain a cold-blooded eyewitness. Perhaps. Perhaps not. Here, however, not. It sprang from person to person, three thousand became one soul. From above to below, from one corner of the room to the other. Irresistible, with lightning speed, a monstrous cataract, the elemental set free. He no longer stood above on the rudely built podium, he was next to us, in us, he burrowed around in the innermost recesses, and he crushed us with his servile lust for success to obey, to obliterate oneself, to be beneath, to be nothing. For the first time I understood what it means to be a woman and to succumb to a man, who rapes the woman first against her will and then suddenly with her will, with her burning pains, with lust burning a thousand times more, to be absorbed in him, to grow together with him as if for eternity. Is love therefore only slavery, slavish salvation? He stood up there, he sobbed, he screamed; something inexplicable, primitive, naked, bloody, burst in gushes from him; he could not stop it. There were no more sentences, no articulated words; the satanic soul which was always hidden had pushed to the surface and no one could withstand it. Germany! Germany! Germany! What did the miserable superpower of the doctor, helpless in the battle against death, amount to against him? His superpower was hate, rage, ecstasy, outbreak, battle cry; only far off in the distance, a rainbow after the storm, there shone a brighter space, his pale, flowery, well-behaved ideal of a new, chaste Germany, happy with its sword — a sentimental epilogue to a brutal song of hate. Everyone relaxed. The walls vibrated with applause, and the hymns of his guard were lost in the frenetic uproar.

Then as before, during the Gurkha attacks, hot human blood sprayed my lips. And Angelica, the eternal housekeeper, the noble widow, groaned more deeply than in my arms; shudder after shudder ran over her somewhat withered face, which was sometimes cramped, sometimes relaxed in highest joy, which became again quite childlike, full of gratitude — and purity. She was not my slave but his. I was a man to her; he was a god. I helped her; he performed miracles.

I drove home silently. I had quickly returned to my senses. I had escaped from the spiritual superpower of A.H., for I saw the danger. Perhaps I regretted for a moment what I had done in the fall of 1918. I had wanted to intervene, to act, to control. In my likeness to God, I had wanted to command, but fate had defeated me. I was without power, for I was alone.

At home there was a short message from Heidi — the peatcutter from the moor had been there and had asked that I come as quickly as possible, for his wife was seriously ill. I left Angelica, took my instrument bag; but before I left I went to the window and took out of a niche in the masonry which was covered with ivy the little box which contained the papers about A.H. I read them again. Perhaps they were a weapon against him, a help to those who would not fall prey to him, who did not dare be as blind as the masses were and as he was. I wanted to hide the papers. Perhaps they could still be of use to the world.

While I was on the way to the moor, a healthy weariness came over me. I was happy that in a short time I would return home and sleep soundly. Something occurred to me then which I had not thought about before — his severe lack of sleep and his complete detachment from love, his insatiableness, the corroding fire of his being which sucked everything to itself and which consumed everything. Perhaps that was the reason he was so fanatic, so narrow-minded, so unchivalrous, so evil, so hate-filled — because love as well as sleep had been denied him.

It was a cold night with clear stars; the moor was frozen — one could move forward with confidence. The Oster Lakes were like solid ground. The ice did not give under my feet. This shortened my way. I soon reached the spot where my life had been in danger. I planned to bury the little box at that point. There no one would suspect its presence. Unfortunately I had not figured on the ground being hard as stone, so I let it be for the time being. I went to the peatcutter's, cared for his wife, and returned home.

When I took the box out of its hiding place behind the ivy the next day, it seemed to me that it was not in the same position. It does not matter, I thought; it has not been opened. The second time I succeeded in burying it deep enough in the moor. I told myself that I must dig it up before the beginning of the warm season or it would sink into the morass. The wife of the peatcutter improved beyond expectations, and in a few days she was out of danger. I took no money from the poor people.

I did not stop with this little show of resistance to A.H., which had not been dangerous for me. Helmut came to see me at the request of Captain R. and said that great things were developing. I too had experienced the miracle of A.H.; they were counting on me and expecting something. Great goals require great financial resources. I looked at him in astonishment, for he had to know that my receipts were small and barely sufficed for a livelihood. Angelica possessed hardly anything anymore, since the depreciation of the war loans had wiped out her savings. When I learned of that I did not rejoice, because my prophecy in 1916 had been made true by the inflation. I sympathized with her, comforted her, and tried to reduce her fanatic hate for Weimar, which she held responsible for the catastrophe.

She agreed, however, only on the surface after kisses and caresses. She actually remained fanatical and stubborn. And as much as the aging woman lay at my feet, as humbly as she waited for my caresses, nonetheless there sometimes lurked in her eyes something like hate, and I saw that she did not forgive me for the humiliation which I had never demanded nor wanted.

In no way could we give very much for the great cause of A.H., even if we wanted to. But Helmut smiled indulgently from above about my misunderstanding. I should fetch a certain sum of money which had been gathered in a small northern Italian city by anonymous donors for the battle against the world Bolshevik-Jewish conspiracy, and I should bring it here as a person trusted by A.H. I counted as a Democrat. That would make the mission easier, he said more cynically than I had ever known him to be. But he did not know me either. I did not ponder long; I refused. Helmut could not believe it and Angelica even less. He threatened me, and I saw that he feared evil consequences for me. But I was firm. I went farther. I became active again in the Democratic party, for it had come to me during A.H.'s speech that it was no longer the time for the scientific observer, for the objective eyewitness of the destruction of the world. A.H. was for ruthless war; he was a soldier, an insane soldier, but a soldier. He did not think of peace, armistice, pardon, agreement. "Always go ahead." All means were right. The attack was perhaps not the best justification, but it was right in itself. "The people see at all times in the ruthless attack on an enemy the proof of its own right." That was his word.

Could we set something similar on the other side in juxtaposition? We could not. We had identified ourselves too much with the enemy. That was our deathly weakness. We lacked naïve brutality as well as naïve sentimentality — the fist, the tear, the lie.

One does not descend into the mass without ridding oneself of the scruples and the conscience which ennoble the individual. We wanted to work with old methods in a new era in which servants had become masters and strength was everything. He was strong who had the most votes. It was difficult to win them with the truth. No politics can be played entirely without lies. But we attempted to get along with the least possible coloring of the truth. On the nationalist side no lie was big enough. Yes, the size of the lie, the exaggeration which had mounted beyond the power to grasp, and the swindling made success certain. And made him secure. His fanatic lies had results. Our half-truths did not.

I attended one more mass assembly but without succumbing to him. I heard him say that Soviet Jews had slowly tortured thirty million Russians to death. "And while now in Russia millions starve and die, the Jewish minister Tschitscherin* rides around Europe in an express train with his staff of two hundred Soviet Jews and is entertained by nude dancers." The absurd was tangible. Tschitscherin was of an old, pure Russian family; there never had been even a hint of nude dances. It was impossible that one out of every four of the one hundred and thirty million Russians could have been slowly tortured to death. Nonetheless — or maybe just because of it — the people believed it, for they could not conceive how anyone could imagine something so devilish, so extraordinary, so stupid.

But they were just as unable to imagine how a person like Oswald Schwarz II or A.H. by the strength of his determination to lie could force himself into blindness — and yet both had done it, and both had unwillingly let their eyes be opened only by the superior force of my desire as a doctor.

Now I had no more power over the man on the podium. I had to consider myself fortunate that he had none over me. I often sat in the front row and tried to catch his eye. It was impossible. He saw nothing.

* Tschitscherin was the Soviet Minister of Foreign Affairs, 1918–1931.

The blind hatred against the Jews returned again and again — it was the mysterious core of his soul. I knew well that I had cured him forever from his hysterical blindness, for a time from his hysterical sleeplessness, but not even for a second from his hatred of the Jews. Had he fallen prey perhaps to a Jewish woman, a *Judt,* in his time of misery in Vienna? Was his chastity voluntary or compulsory? Could he no longer give himself to a woman of his race, of his German blood? Did this torture him, did this make him sleepless, did this make him loveless, insatiable, and did this give him his monstrous, fanatic power? Did he have this splinter under his fingernail so that he struck out with such a brutal fist? Behind his songs of hate and his storms about virtue there often lay something like desperation. His hatred was a source of monstrous power. No consideration, no mildness, no reason, no love restrained him.

"The Soviet star is the Star of David," he said, "the symbol of the synagogue." Actually, of course, the Star of David is six-pointed, for it consists of two triangles joined; the Soviet star, however, is a five-pointed star drawn with one uninterrupted stroke. As a former painter, he must have known that. And yet he lied and believed that he spoke the truth. He blinded himself a little in such a detail just as he blinded himself magnificently in great matters. And with each of his lies he won more power than any reasonable zealot of the truth with a "demonstrable fact." People believed him; they did not believe someone like Rathenau. "The Star of David is the symbol of a race over the world, from Vladivostok to the West — of the rule of Jewry. The golden star signified for the Jew the glistening gold, the hammer designated the impact of Masonry. The sickle, the horrible terror!" The sickle, the symbol of the harvest, the peaceful thing shining on the green hills of mowed grass — the symbol of horrible terror! Angelica believed it, she swore by him. For a long time it had been impossible to reason with her. She who was so slavish to me did not let herself be robbed of one iota of her new gospel. And she knew many South German Jews. She had always praised their friendliness, their gratitude, their integrity, when she spoke of them as patients or as relatives of the Jewish patients in Kaiser's clinic. She still had a few pieces of jewelry which Jewish patients or their families had given her, and she wore this jewelry to the assemblies.

They were about the last remnants of her earlier prosperity. Just as she had been impoverished almost to beggarhood by the depreciation of the money, just so millions of others had suffered. The Ruhr was occupied. The mark was scarcely worth the paper it was printed on. Everything was in chaos. The French had confiscated the printing presses for banknotes and had increased the flood of paper still more.

Weimar had no more authority. South Germany wanted to secede from North Germany, or more accurately, the fanatic nationalist party which A.H. had given a tremendous boost refused to support Weimar, the system, if there should be war against the Poles. But it furthered the most intensive preparations for a war of the South against the North, against the home of Marxism, the pestilential proletarian land. South Germany with its strong masses of peasants wanted to conquer North Germany. The South German troops refused obedience to the North; the gold reserves and the supplies of foreign currency were not allowed over the borders. In the spring of 1923 the last separation between the healthy and the sick parts of the realm was to be ruthlessly completed with a bloody edge. Germans against Germans? So what? The highest authorities in Bavaria were united with A.H. They were Germans first, then civil servants, he boasted. That is, they ought to break their oath of office for the sake of their fanatic nationalist goals.

Many viewed all this with dread. Resistance was still possible. The masses were only stupefied by necessity, oppressed by the flood, torn loose from their old sites, but not drowned. They were not yet poisoned; for the moment they were blinded.

I spoke often in assemblies. I devoted every moment I could free from my practice to the cause. The number of our adherents grew. Contributions came, even young people came. If the government had been more energetic, if the "system" had been less regimented, bolder, more stimulating, much more could have been achieved.

But they thought that they had to be impartial to both the right and the left. They weakened their defenders and made their inexorable and insatiable enemies strong. The government was the eyewitness of its own decline, and when a miracle rescued it, it did not comprehend. It had never understood its enemies. It assumed they were of their own kind. It trusted their solemn promises, took seriously their "word of honor."

So it came to the putsch of November 1923. The army believed that the insurrection which A.H. had organized had been created for their benefit; the good old bourgeois circles, the officials like von Kahr,* who were behind A.H. with money and influence, believed that it was a counterrevolution that would return the old dynasty, still loved, to the throne. But A.H. thought only of himself. No one had credited him with that, maybe not even he himself. He was supposed to be a second miracle.

He had jumped, but too short. The Bavarian State Police, on whom A.H. had depended, shot sharply. Ludendorff,† at the head of A.H.'s train, went coldly through the fire. The ministers, surprised for one night, awakened to clarity the next morning.

Everything seemed lost. No one could attack Ludendorff, who had again not correctly judged the "war goals." All Germany had to remain loyal to him once again, although he had lost the Great War in such a grandiose manner and although he had betrayed Weimar for a second time.

Like Ludendorff, A.H., too, by a miracle, had escaped unwounded from the crackling rain of the police bullets. The miracle extended farther on his heels. Was I not the one who had performed a miracle on him, had made him from a blind person to a seeing person? He came to trial and mercy prevailed. He left the trial almost as victor over his judges, over the betrayed betrayers. He was condemned to five years' imprisonment. When he came out of prison six months later, Germany's position, to his misfortune, had been truly improved. Once again there was a firm currency. Thanks to Briand and Stresemann,‡ the occupation of the Ruhr had ended. People were able to think of themselves; they worked, hoped, and slowly rebuilt.

Vroni, thanks to a little capital from my mother's bequest, had married a small cigarette manufacturer of advanced age, in whose

* Gustav von Kahr, Minister of Bavaria 1923–1924, defeated the Nazi putsch.
† Erich Ludendorff, General in the German army, was active in Nazi circles.
‡ Aristide Briand was French Minister of Foreign Affairs, 1925–1932. Gustav Stresemann was German Minister of Foreign Affairs, 1923–1929.

factory the money was being put to work. He was undemanding, industrious, pleasant, beer-loving. He had a big family for whom Vroni had to keep house. My half brother became a machinist in a large factory. My half sister was a kind of servant to her mother in the house, more than a servant but unpaid. They were still poor, but everything was obviously improving.

I had separated from Angelica. I no longer trusted her. I saw her as an "impure vessel"; she probably felt the same way about me. A.H. was pure; I was not. I was relieved. This extravagant passion had not been good for me. She was too warm, but I was not warmed by her. I took an older woman from the area as a servant. She kept the house well, but she could not help me in any way in my profession.

I saw von Kaiser only occasionally, Helmut never. He purposely avoided me. He still had faith in A.H., in fact, more than ever before. A.H. was and remained for him a herald of the German God, yes, a German Christ in person. Vroni and her children, too, were loyal in their adoration of the man, for whom she had sympathy because he had been tortured more than Christ on the cross. Actually, he had recuperated in prison and had gained considerable weight. But she did not want to believe that; she wept bitter tears about his agony and torture. Apart from his heavenly oratorical gift, by means of which the Lord God spoke through him, she had been enchanted like Angelica by his chaste, nonfleshly being, by the fact that he had not touched a bite of meat for years, that he had kept his distance from women, that he wore no golden ring, that he wanted nothing for himself — and was so grateful for love and tenderness. It was the glowing faith of the first Christians.

In 1924 Dr. Kaiser, Victoria's father, was seriously ill. I had visited him often of late, in part to see Victoria again. I had not been able to free myself from her. As a mature man, I was in love for the first time. She remained cool when I came after the long separation. But gradually something relaxed in her, and as she began to cry at the deathbed of her father she took both of my hands, as my mother had once done, in order to hold me. It was the moment for which I had waited many years. She was at the boundary of her youth, just as I was. She was still very beautiful. I already had some gray hair. I remembered that my mother, too, had become gray rather early. My father had fewer gray hairs than I. He lived now in a happy marriage with his Heidi, was building happily and contentedly a house for himself for a second time. They had no children. Since, however, my father loved children, he often had his illegitimate children come. They considered the visits a favor.

My earlier mistress had become friendly with them and wanted to move into a little tower room in the new villa. She was heart and soul bound up with the blond Heidi. All of them — my father, Heidi, Angelica — came to congratulate me in a sweet-sour fashion on my engagement to Victoria. I also sent Helmut word; he did not answer my letter.

His father wrote to me from Italy, where he lived with Katinka — it was not apparent whether or not in peace. I did not begrudge him anything. I was very grateful to all who had helped me earlier, since a time of long, peaceful happiness seemed to dawn in my house for me. How could I forget Kaiser? I was respected in my party, which still made progress, though only moderately. Youth, women came in small numbers. We were too sober for them, we did not flatter them enough; probably we did not know how to talk to them, excite them, and intoxicate them.

Victoria finally accepted the idea that I was politically active. She too after many joyless years had become happy; she expected a child and was resigned to fate, as I was. Sometimes I wondered why we had not been united long before. But they were pointless thoughts. Why? We had much work and were happy in the evening when we had accomplished everything.

The condition of the realm after the surprising flowering from 1923 to 1929 became gradually more and more critical. Unemployment increased slowly but steadily. Industrial reorganization, undertaken much too suddenly and without sufficient financial reserves, took its revenge. Vroni complained that her husband had replaced a great many workers with new American cigarette machines, but the customers were lacking, for the workers had been their best customers. She was appalled that her son had been fired from the factory without reason. "Marxists! Jews!" she muttered. At first he had hung around the house but then, perhaps because of idealistic reasons, had joined his idol A.H., and had become one of the uniformed but not quite legal troops, the SA.* He received a small salary which was paid irregularly. Since he also received unemployment compensation from the government which he was trying to undermine, he could even furnish some money for the household. The SA became increasingly stronger. Unemployment spread somewhat more quickly; I noticed it among my patients, and with it the misery and discontent swelled. A new wait for the Messiah, an indictment against Weimar, the hate for officials, for the bigwigs, for the members of the parliament, the parasites, the despair over the existing legal order, over the system, and in fact over God. Parliamentary elections took place at shorter and shorter intervals.

However, no one anticipated anything decisive from the old parties. The National Revolutionary party of A.H., which like the old Fatherland party wanted to be one party above all others and which had risen like a phoenix out of ashes after the collapse of 1923, gradually attracted all the doubters, all those confused about the future.

In the meantime a son, Robert, and three years later a daughter, Lise, were born to us. We were all happy. I would never have believed that Victoria and I could have such happiness. We thought it would last forever, to our natural ends.

I had to work harder in order to provide a livelihood; I had to employ more people, and politics could not take as much of my time as before. Everything became more and more expensive. But I had to reduce my fees, divide my time more carefully, forgo much, and again calculate by the penny. Our party was at a standstill.

The Socialists at the next elections had no great losses, but the extreme right parties like that of A.H. and the extreme left like the Communists held tremendous attraction for young voters, who were captivated by agitation and were without work — in many cases they had never worked. They also attracted those who had been uprooted by the war, the revolution and inflation, who were disenfranchised and were again losing the last bit of solid ground under their feet. Everything was as it had been on the moor.

Anarchy from the left and the right ruled under a thin coating of order. There remained, if one reasoned logically, no other govern-

* Sturmabteilung (storm troopers, Brown Shirts).

mental form for the German empire than the parliamentary republic — such as this downgraded Weimar — or the return to the imperial dynasty. The old honorable president was loyal to the imperial house, and he made no secret of it, but he realized that its return was impossible without a revolution, and so he faithfully served the system. He was respected. A.H. was loved and hated. In the meantime he had conquered North Germany; the masses of workers listened to him — some with love, others with hate — he left no one neutral. The unemployed rallied around him with immeasurable hopes; his party grew like a landslide. In a short time it increased from twelve to a hundred and seven to two hundred and thirty votes in the parliament. He himself was a foreigner; he had remained an Austrian citizen. He went about in a simple fashion, worked with indescribable energy, only for his cause — that is, for himself. He accepted no honors. He ruled indisputably over a half-million SA men, who had been militarily organized with the help of Captain R., who had returned from exile in Bolivia. The money to support this huge army came from the heavy industries who were afraid of the Communists. He spoke, and the more powerful he became, the more monstrous was the power of his fanatic speeches which captured everyone.

I too had been approached, first with the demand that I join the new party, then with the demand to pay a larger contribution. I refused both.

Late one evening I was told that a man in a party uniform wanted to speak to me. He did not, however, want to come into my consultation room, but waited outside in the garden in the pouring rain. It was Helmut. He did not shake my hand nor did he take off his cap. He told me very curtly that there was a rumor "among authoritative persons" which he did not believe but about which he had to tell me as a "former friend." I was supposed to have papers, documents and records, about *him* (he did not mention a name, everyone was bound to know who it was). I should give them to him. They would be destroyed. I would suffer no unpleasantness because of this suppression of records. I refused this, too.

I had retrieved the papers from their hiding place in the moor long ago and kept them in a little fireproof safe. My wife wanted to know what I had discussed outside. I answered her evasively.

Just as in my youth, when I had written my diary on pieces of wood in hieroglyphics, I wanted to keep my secret. I did not want to reveal myself entirely to my wife, whom I loved with all my heart, any more than I had wanted to reveal myself to my mother. I had learned nothing from the dreary experiences of my youth. At that time I made my mother distrustful, and I lost her love because of this distrust. I certainly paid dearly for this innocent secret.

I did not believe in any new revolution which could be inflamed by A.H. In my opinion it was senseless. It could not, I was quite convinced, improve the circumstances of the broad social classes. There were only three fixed points for A.H. — the first was the Führer concept in the style of Mussolini, a single ruler, a dictatorship dependent entirely on force, a popular emperor in brown uniform. Because his home was Braunau, he had chosen brown as his favorite color, and his million SA men were dressed in brown shirts and uniforms. The second point was the rearming of Germany for the war of revenge. If the victory of 1918 had brought the allies — the French, English, Americans, and the others — no blessing, and if their enemy, Germany, beaten almost to extinction, had recovered in spite of its defeat in a few years, what could another world war with new millions of human sacrifices and new destruction bring in lasting benefits? Was it not better to think of peace before a war rather than afterward? Even A.H., regardless of how insatiable, could not swallow all of Europe and the rest of the world, too? The third point was the hatred of the Jews. I could not believe that the satisfying of this hate against a minuscule splinter of people could make the victors over *der Judt* happy. But A.H. calculated better. He figured on the monstrous power of a lie, or ruthless attacking hatred; he always acted with brutal power, even when he could have achieved his goal without it. He built on three basic characteristics of people — their bestiality, their weakness, and their cowardice. These drives are in every person. In quiet times they are suppressed by reason and law. In times of danger they are unleashed and go their own way. I, a doctor, a researcher, a cold-blooded man, had succumbed to the satanic soul in war and had acted bestially. If a man like A.H. was able to subjugate millions to him, even to obedience to death, were there limits set for him? Did he have anything to fear but death?

But were we, the people of the middle, of moderation, really the weak ones if we were united? The extreme left, devotees of power without opposition, a brutal dictatorship, just like that of the right, certainly did not unite with us, the moderate parties. It joined the extreme right. The Communists did not see an enemy in A.H., but in moderate socialist democracy. The parliament was dissolved, elected again, and dissolved again because the Communists together with A.H.'s National Socialists constituted a front, a blockade, a majority.

It was time to elect a president again. The old marshal was re-elected by the moderate parties. He received a huge majority. Were we therefore saved? Were we in the majority? But we had not calculated that the straightforward energy of the old man of honor would be bent when his old fatherly heart was troubled. His son was compromised in a bribery scandal. Only the most extreme measures could save him and the caste of the marshal. Only A.H., who had just been defeated, could rescue the victor! The president of the realm was first and foremost father, officer, noble, then president and eyewitness, highest judge over the parties. He shied from scandal. He yielded. A.H. became chancellor. But the constitution still stood. Civil rights had not yet been abrograted.

Now A.H. had the German parliament building set on fire. What did the parliament building mean to him and his party? Less than nothing. For he had always viewed the parliament with contempt. But for the masses it signified something as the evidence of parliamentary government, of freedom. But the new chancellor of the empire succeeded in spreading dismay and fear in the citizenry while the flames shot out of the building. He who knew no other freedom than his own set himself up by virtue of his own right as the defender of freedom, as the protector of parliamentary rights, as the keeper of order. He, the revolutionary, was for the old liberal tradition. The danger came, according to his speeches (perhaps he too believed his fantasies), from the extreme left, the Communists.

The Communists had set fire to the Reichstag. It was they and they alone who wanted revolution and the destruction of everything old, good, and free. They had to be made innocuous. They must die so that Germany might live. First, he ordered the suppression of all civil liberties. No more rights for labor; no assemblies; no free-

147

dom of speech; no freedom of the press; no private letters or telegrams anymore. Unlimited rights for the police, who were to shoot
immediately. The harmless rubber truncheon was replaced with a
revolver. Abolition of the legal processes.

Everyone thought that this would last only for a short, critical
period. There were no measures against the Jews. In fact, they were
promised the continuation of their lifestyle if they were well behaved. What could they, a minute minority, less than one in a hundred, do? They were silent like everyone; they sought refuge with
each other as everyone else did, and they trembled as did the entire
country — with the exception of the devotees of the terrorists. New
elections were held. A.H. had promised the president that he would
not organize any. He broke his word, cynically innocent, as he had
broken it to the generals in 1923. The elections did not give the
National Socialists a majority. Only together with the hesitant,
poorly directed German Nationalists did they have one per cent
above half of all the votes. The Führer frankly promised the German Nationalists eternal participation in power. In a few months
they were excluded. By this method the small minority of A.H.'s
which was not afraid of anything obtained power over a feuding
majority.

Who would have dared to accuse the most German of all Germans
of breaking his word? He always believed what he said. But only
so long as he said it or remembered it. But his memory changed and
deceived him, the poor fellow. He was really poor from the point of
view of a healthy person, a doctor.

A miracle had happened. How could a man like this, an unemployed painter from Vienna, become the most powerful man in the
German empire unless it was a miracle? Where did the lie end,
where did the miracle begin? He himself believed in miracles,
heard voices, was grateful for Providence. God was with him, he
screamed; God had been with him. Today as in 1918. My word had
become fearfully and divinely true: he had helped himself and
God had helped him.

A.H. was no longer the man with the narrow corporal's stripe on
his shoulder flap and the dubious Iron Cross, First Class. He was
the highest and soon after that the only one in the nation. He
could have been silent. The Communists were annihilated, just like

the bourgeois parties, just like everything except himself. But he had a reporter of an American newspaper come, and he said to him, word for word: "In that night of the fire in the Reichstag and in the Berlin castle, as cries for help came from all over Germany by telephone, telegraph and radio about the imminent Bolshevik treachery and revolution, I determined to use ruthlessly all the power at my command, all powers of attack. The revelations which were made two hours later gave me the right. In Berlin alone we found during the immediate occupation of public buildings, including the university, the library and numerous Berlin district halls, the supplies of arson: fuses, combustible wool soaked in gasoline, and explosives. If I had not acted promptly in that decisive hour for order and peace against the Bolshevik incendiarism, not only the Reichstag and the palace but all public buildings of Germany would have gone up in flames, and who knows, maybe all of the Occident would have been a pile of ashes. The coming legal trials will open the eyes of the world about the sensations of that night, which are derived from the material found which up to now because of the investigation could not be revealed. The evidence guarantees the uncovering of a Bolshevik world plot." So many words, so many lies! So much denunciation, so much fantasy! Nothing was true in these comments broadcast throughout the whole world, which particularly in England and America fired the fear of a Bolshevik world plot. The Führer never proved what he had announced; he never even tried to.

If anyone did, I had to know the new master of the world. I had to fear him. I had to flee from him, for he was strong and I was weak. But in the recesses of my heart I was allured and tantalized by the danger. If it is tragic to go to one's destruction with open eyes, then I was tragic. But it was really only tragicomic.

Immediately after the seizure of power, a monstrous, muddy flood of denunciations broke loose. Fathers denounced their sons, sons their fathers, wives their husbands, in the hope of gaining advantages from the new regime — or simply from a desire for revenge, out of hate, out of the meanness of their nature. The low had become high in everything, and whoever had not wanted to bow to the white silk slipper of the pope in Rome or to the sword of a marshal in the old imperial German headquarters came to kiss with pleasure the soles of a man whom numerous people had known as a vagabond on the streets of Vienna. Because he had been so small, because he had emerged out of the swampy, bubbling, silent, primal masses — just that made him so dear to them, and they adored him. He was no longer, as he had first boasted, the John of an approaching Jesus, the herald of a coming hero; he was Jesus and war hero combined in one. They bowed voluptuously to the earth before him, whom a miracle had made a ruler out of nothingness.

I knew the miracle at its source. For I had given him the belief in himself as a divine miracle.

I knew that we, my wife and I, would never be on the side of the sword: my wife, with her clear understanding and goodness, because she had never been there; and I, who for months had waded in blood, because I had returned to other work, and not without success. I was much loved in the area, and even when it was dangerous to shelter me, convinced adherents of the idol had not refused me asylum — in fact, they offered it voluntarily. It was the same kind of people, and I say it emphatically, who carried out the terrible atrocities in concentration camps and underground prison dungeons on poor helpless prisoners who then risked their own lives to help me.

For the first time it became clear to me that man is something terrible but also something godlike.

When the first rumors came to us that they were searching for me, I was still holding office hours every day from two to four, paying my taxes regularly; I had a telephone and a small automobile. I thought that the rumor reflected some confusion in names. After all, there had been two men named Oswald Schwarz; why not two with my name?

But I did take precautions concerning the papers. I had thought of sending them in a sealed envelope to Councillor von Kaiser, as professional papers. He had gathered a vast quantity of similar records, only they did not concern a corporal A.H. Then I gave up that idea. He was old, he could die. His wife could destroy the papers after his death. They must not be lost.

Did I think of publishing them to show the world, at least the foreign countries, how the superman, the demigod, had been only fifteen years earlier, how he had appeared at that time to science, to the completely impartial eyewitness? No, I did not dare do that. Not because I feared the consequences, about which I was not sure, but out of respect for the doctor's professional secrets. So I abided by the unwritten law of professional honor. He knew no honor. I could not live without honor.

My wife advised me with tears in her eyes to burn the records. No, I could not decide on that either. I wanted to demonstrate my courage by keeping them. Again and not for the last time I made myself strong and considered the tears of my wife as sentimentality which often overtakes women who are expecting. I satisfied myself with a stratagem for keeping the papers but at the same time not being burdened with them. I sent them, with another name as sender, to a third name, general delivery, at a post office in M. Such mailings remained untouched in the post office for three months; then I could go there, address it again, and let it lie another three months in a different post office. It would be dangerous to do it twice in the same post office. The postal authorities were fanatic adherents of A.H. They quite willingly listened to telephone conversations, searched through letters and packages, and were not ashamed to be betrayers and hangmen of people who had taken professional integrity for granted.

My wife breathed more easily when the papers were out of the house. She persuaded me to renew my passport, which was valid for the entire family, and also to get one for her alone and to send some savings to Switzerland.

This was all still possible and permitted in the first months after the takeover of A.H. No one at that time foresaw the terrible enslavement which he spread afterward, step by step, without protest from the masses, even with approval, which soon exceeded any measures that despots of the past had used for gagging every kind of freedom.

During that time I received an anonymous warning letter. I never took anonymous letters seriously — I had my reasons for that. Shortly after the death of my mother my wife had received such a letter, which said that she should hold no hope for me, that I had promised my mother on her deathbed not to marry a Jewess. This anonymous report had unfortunately moved my poor wife to show me a cold demeanor for years, to keep herself forcibly at a distance until we finally spoke at the deathbed of her father. I can think of only one person who could have written that letter – Angelica, who wanted to prevent our marriage. What interest, however, could she have in urging me to go abroad immediately? I thought of Helmut, but Helmut acted straightforwardly and would have found another way. Thus he came to us later, and I owe him my life. It was no one else, I discovered later, than that inexperienced doctor about whom the priest of S. had told me years before. He was still in the neighborhood, in the little town of T., a fanatical follower of A.H., a doctor who learned nothing new, never changed his views, never doubted himself, and whose patients came constantly to me. Often I refused them, but they were not to be gainsaid in their fear about their health and life. I could not stop them from wanting to entrust themselves to me rather than to him. He wanted to get rid of me. He knew that there was evidence against me, but nothing against the written law.

In the chaos of unleashed passions there was no law anymore. There was no more freedom, no orderly legal procedure which represented the interests of the state and of the accused impartially; objectivity, justice, freedom were no more.

He meant well toward me. But my conscience seemed clear to me, and the danger must have stimulated me just like that time when, as a child, I had entered the barracks without goal or purpose under the pressure of withstanding a danger and let a stupid horse trample me. After all, I had intended no harm. I had come with bread in my hand.

One day in the summer of 1933 my father came late in the evening and said that he had to speak to me privately. He did not love my wife, partly because as a convinced National Socialist he saw her only as a Jewess, but he did have grandfatherly feelings for his grandson and granddaughter. My wife wanted to hear the conversation, and she had a right to do so. But I did not want to contradict him, for then he would leave. I did not want that to happen, and so I asked her to let us leave. He took me out to the street, where my little car stood with dimmed lights, and we went back and forth several times along the lake road which leads from my house to T., but we avoided the road to S., where we had many more acquaintances than in T.

He wasted no words. He told me that he knew from the best sources that shortly there would be a thorough search of my house. I was not in favor because of my marriage to a Jewess, my membership in the German Peace Association, and my liberal speeches on behalf of the Democratic party, which had long since been dissolved. But I was generally beloved in the area as a doctor. In fact, I had advocates in the party. His wife and even Angelica had done everything possible for me. I was indebted to them and to my comrade Helmut for my having been left in peace. Others with less reason were already in concentration camps.

Since the inauguration of A.H. as chancellor, Führer of the party, and dictator of the whole empire, concentration camps had been established in old factories, deserted barracks, empty ruined castles. (In such a castle the two young assassins of Rathenau had committed suicide; they had since become national heroes — there were pilgrimages to their grave, a national shrine.) The camps were supposed to be a "necessity," based on the humane reasoning that people who were in disfavor with the party must be protected from the righteous indigination of the masses in order to save their lives. It was security imprisonment without legal procedure, without public prosecutor and indictment, as it had been used during the war as a military necessity against such agitators as Rosa Luxemburg and Karl Liebknecht.* No legal decision was necessary for transfer to such a camp; the police were all-sufficient. There was no defender because there was no indictment. The camps were surrounded with barbed wire which carried high, deadly, electric currents. They were surrounded by walls, protected by machine guns; a watchtower made possible continuous observation of the camp. Behind the barbed wires lived a great number of people, from several hundred to ten thousand, hermetically sealed off from the rest of the world. Terrifying reports about the treatment of these prisoners were repeated in whispers. Up to then I had not wanted to believe. I asked my father about them, for as a good National Socialist he had visited such a camp, and in fact had served there for a time.

* Rosa Luxemburg, a socialist politician, was a leader of the Spartacus revolt. She was shot as a traitor in 1919. Karl Liebknecht was a leader of the Spartacus movement and a co-worker with Rosa Luxemburg. He also was assassinated in 1919.

He did not answer but took me by the arm, so firmly that it hurt, and finally said that that was not relevant, I should not wait until my enemies had overcome my friends. Life was better in Switzerland than in a concentration camp. In any case, he gave me a bundle of Swiss currency which he had saved since the World War. "Now in the Third Reich I do not need the money anymore," he said. "It is too bad that you married this Jewish woman. Pardon the hard word — it concerns her race, not her personally. She cannot help it. Why did you not obey your mother? In this one point the bigoted sourpuss — don't be angry when I say this, but she soured my whole life and yours too — in this point she gave you good advice. But what is done is done. Victoria is really an exception. She does not have Jewish coloring but is as blond as Heidi. Perhaps she is a bastard and has a few drops of decent blood, and then your children would not be half-Jewish but only a quarter. What I am doing, and I am doing and risking a lot, I do only on your account. You have always despised my unprepossessing manner; now you see, however, that Heidi, Angelica, and I are there where it is right. We are in good standing; in your case it is different. Now listen to my advice. Drive to Switzerland tomorrow for a rest. That is permitted. Go alone; your wife will follow later. Meet in Basel or somewhere else in Switzerland. I'll write you, general delivery, without a signature — you know my handwriting. I'll give you the news. Leave the children with me; Heidi will take good care of them. After all, they are mine, too, and I'll vouch for them. Wait there. In a few months or years there will be more peace in the country, and if you have been quiet and have not stirred and have done your work well, you won't suffer. You are supposed to have papers about the Führer? I can't believe it. You are much too intelligent to keep something compromising, and it would be madness to take them along to Switzerland, for you know very well that our arm reaches far."

I realized that his plan was good, but I still wanted to be smarter than he. We returned to our house, but he did not leave me alone again. I called the doctor in T. whom I have mentioned, who, I knew, had little to do and could take over my patients immediately, among whom there was no one in critical condition. He knew of my decision before I had finished talking; the Brown Shirts were clannish and had no secrets among themselves. He was very friendly and wished me a speedy recovery, for I spoke of a health leave. My wife stood by the telephone — my father, too — and she listened to everything, pale as death but composed. She said to my father, who found the conversation painful, that she was ready to make any sacrifice which would benefit me and the children, even to divorce me. But she could not give up the children. I told her that I would never leave her. My father grew impatient. We finally decided that my wife should wait only two or three days for two reasons. She had just had a middle ear infection and still had some fever and was not equal to traveling, and second, she wanted to be sure that I was over the border.

I was uneasy in spirit. Something of the monster, grinding, crushing, consuming, which I had not experienced for many years, came over me, but I saw how quiet she was, how much in those difficult moments she resembled my mother, who had become all the more composed the more difficult life became. I submitted to both of them, my father and my wife; we agreed that I would go to the Hotel Grauer Bär in Berne; she would report to me there, and I would arrange everything so that we could live there for a time until order, justice and law had returned to Germany.

I took my father along to M., let him out, and drove on to the suburb G.,* but toward morning I returned to the post office, got my papers, and laid them very casually in a fold of the top of the car. They were not noticed at the border, which I crossed about noon. I drove to Basel, relieved, happy and relaxed. In the afternoon I went to the Federal Central Bank, where I had deposited my money. I rented a safe deposit box in my name and that of my wife and put the papers in it. Then I drove quietly to Berne, where I went to the Grauer Bär. Everything had gone so fast that I hardly believed it. Everything was quiet, and it seemed to me that I had been in too much of a hurry, that my anxiety had been extreme, and that I could have continued in my practice as an innocent and blameless person and have stayed at home.

I waited in the middle of the peaceful environment of a free city and of free Swiss citizens in growing fear for the reports from home and, above all, for the telegram that would announce the arrival of

* Garching.

my wife, which did not come. I had taken a room with a double bed and had bought a bouquet of beautiful flowers, but I already had dreary forebodings.

I was desperate even before I lost my footing, and therefore I betrayed myself. A telegram came. The elevator boy brought it and held out his hand for a tip. I scanned the telegram and, crushed, I read: YOUR WIFE IMPRISONED FOR TIME BEING BECAUSE OF TAX EVA-SION STOP TAX RECEIPTS NOT TO BE FOUND STOP RETURN NO DANGER CHILDREN HEALTHY STOP HEIL H. FATHER.

I collapsed on my chair and the boy brought me water. I read the message of ill fortune again.

I noticed that something was wrong. My father would have called my wife by name, and the suspicion of imprisonment because of tax evasion was so absurd that I knew right away that the secret police wanted to lure me over the border to get my papers. But immediately I began to blame myself, to berate myself that I could hesitate for even a moment to rescue my beloved wife. I had to go back. At once. Blindly. Without thought. I could never, I said to myself, leave my wife and my children in the lurch.

I packed in a hurry and dashed out of the hotel so quickly that I forgot to cancel my room, to make arrangements about my car in the garage, and to tell the porter of my departure.

Now something really tragicomic occurred. I had taken an open taxi and we were going rapidly toward the station. As I came into the neighborhood of the station I saw another open taxi approach-ing, likewise going fast, and in that one sat my wife. I screamed and waved as the two taxis passed each other. But the woman did not look up, did not turn. She surely could not have failed to hear my voice? The explanation was much simpler, and I could have arrived at it immediately. First, my wife's hearing had been diminished by the middle ear infection; second, she had cotton in her ear; third, she was not expecting to hear my voice in the midst of traffic. The simplest course, which clear, logical reason should have followed, was to have the taxi turn around, go back to the hotel, and to as-sure myself whether it was really my wife whom I had seen. But I did not want to believe it. I did not have strength enough for a happy faith. I had become distrustful, and in this most important moment I suffered from it. My mother had been right.

I continued my trip, let the skeptical psychiatrist in me speak; he diagnosed it as a hallucination, a daydream, wishful thinking, which had made by wife appear to me while she was really imprisoned by the Secret State Police. The next train for Germany left in twelve minutes. Before I bought my ticket, I did telephone the hotel without really expecting any good news. I asked, "Has a lady asked to speak to me?" "No, Doctor, no one has come." Later I discovered that my wife had had the same idea as I — to buy flowers. This had delayed her a few minutes. Was it coincidence or fate? And so she entered the hotel at the same moment that I climbed into the express train which took me back to Germany.

In M. I took a taxi and drove home. The house was deserted, the doors sealed. My first task was to find my father. "What are you doing here?" he cried, growing pale; even Angelica trembled.

"Why didn't you stay in Berne?" she whispered.

"Where is my wife?" I asked.

"She left long ago," answered Heidi.

I wanted to see my children and was waiting for them when several SS[*] men in their black uniforms entered, greeted the two women politely, approached me, put me in their midst, and spoke to me by name. I went with them and met my children, who were not permitted to kiss me. The SS took me in a huge new Mercedes to Munich. The trip, which had taken me an hour and a quarter in the clattery taxi, was completed in a little over thirty minutes.

They gave no answers to my questions. In M. they took me to police headquarters, and I was given a single cell after they took my papers, money, watch, passport, keys — including the new one for the safe deposit box — bootlaces and suspenders, and inspected me from top to bottom, even to the welt in my shoes, as if I had been able to hide something valuable there. I spent a night which I cannot describe.

I will describe the immediate future only briefly. Some experiences are so horrible that one can perhaps, with all one's effort, summon the strength to live through them, if one has to. But I do not have the strength to relive them in their entirety, and no one can force me to. At least I cannot do it today.

In the next days the mental torture began. I was questioned without interruption for hours, for days. The accusers took turns.

[*] Schutzstaffel. This was originally Hitler's bodyguard and was ultimately responsible for control of all occupied countries.

When one group could not continue, others took their place; only I dared not stir. I told the truth. I confessed everything. I defended myself only with truthful assertions. But they seemed to want something else. They believed that I would break down, but I remained master of myself.

I told them what had happened in the hospital in P. in 1918. I agreed that I had made notes about the facts. But I had not taken the official papers with me. If they were missing, someone else had disposed of them, perhaps someone in the war ministry or an officer of the army who had been interested in A.H. as an agitator. They listened to me, wrote, asked more questions. Every few hours they let me leave. The urge to relieve myself was so strong that they had to excuse me. If they had followed their inclinations, I would not have had even those three minutes of rest in the lavatory. The dreadful torture lasted for thirteen days. I did not eat anymore and was reduced to a skeleton. I did not sleep. I stopped thinking. I had become an animal, but I had to act like a human being. Then one day they abruptly ended the inquisition, transported me with others to the concentration camp of D.,* and housed me in one of the wooden barracks.

I had determined not to yield to the temptation of suicide. I knew now that my wife had been rescued and that was one reason for me to live. She was in safety. I therefore had to do everything not to betray myself a second time by killing myself as my captors wished. They had returned my suspenders. I had thin but tough laces in my shoes. I had handkerchiefs. A person with great strength of will can choke himself; he can hang himself, even without a footstool and a window latch. He does not need a light. All he has to have is a fixed determination. He must be a Spartan.

I will not describe that camp; it was like all the others. I will not touch on the story of any of my companions in misfortune; it was like mine. I would never come to an end of this story otherwise. One of them had said to me on the night after my arrival, "Be prepared, man!" It seemed that I had known him earlier; we were, after all, human beings, perhaps from the German Peace Society. I cannot say. I had lost all capacity to think of anything except:

* Dachau.

Don't let yourself be moved to suicide! Hold on! Perhaps you will see your wife and children again. They are alive; you will see them again. Don't let them make you divulge your secret. Hold fast! Don't let yourself be tempted by suicide. This very narrow thought sequence followed its circular path, and I thought of nothing else. I saw and heard nothing. I crouched on the iron bed and adjured myself.

I think that by this means I instinctively found the one way to keep alive — I narrowed my mental horizon, I suggested to myself what I had to think, and I let the superior power of the doctor work in my own case. I stood as eyewitness alongside the prisoner. I commanded myself and I obeyed myself. Torture was before me. I had to be clear in myself. I did not dare to contradict myself; for every contradiction brought me to despair, and despair was only another word for death.

Night came on slowly. At nine o'clock there was always more activity in the cells of the wooden barracks. "Be prepared, man!" I said to myself. I heard the locks clank and the crunching of heavy boots on the sand-strewn paths. They passed my cell. I felt like the child whom the Kaiser-Jew had examined to find the spot for the injection and who had wanted to laugh because of the tickling. But now was not the time for laughter. The walls were thinner than I had thought; I could hear everything that happened. It was not only one who did the beating; there were several. Later I discovered that there were usually three. They did it in rhythm, in chorus. I heard it. When I put my fingers in my ears, I heard it more distinctly. It rose — and there was no end to the moaning. I thought of only one thing — they should stop, they should stop next door. It would be better if they came to me. If they killed me, that was my fate. I did not want to yield. I wanted to hold out. But I wanted to endure the terror myself on my skin, not on my ears and on the throbbing beat of my heart. But what could I do with all my Spartan power against the choking feeling of revulsion, the instinctive trembling, the intestinal cramps, the flood of urine which I could not control? While I took care of my necessity in the corner, screams of pain next door rose to an unrestrained animal cry. It was more frightening than the howl of the tiger. It was more frightening than the cries of pain of the people who died a slow and painful death on the barbed wire of the Western Front, even though their wounds were slight, because no one could get to them through the rain of bullets. Won't they ever stop? That was my only thought. Even that other one — not to commit suicide — which I had hammered so carefully into myself, disappeared.

Then they stopped. Perhaps the victim could endure no more. He merely groaned and moaned in dull tones. But it was even more inhuman to listen to than the earlier, sharply penetrating screams. One more blow hissed through the air. But then the victim next door had no more power to scream, none to groan; it was quiet. The beaters cursed and coughed; perhaps he had come to an end. Then they entered my cubicle; a man with a lantern preceded them. Each one had a horsewhip in his hand: the heavy end in his fist, the thin end whirling tentatively through the air. From the adjacent cell one could hear how the man moved again; there was a rattle in his throat, and the wooden bedstead creaked under him; he moved again and again. It was my turn. I thought at first that they would question me, that they would try to press something out of me through fright. I was glad, if one can speak of being glad in such circumstances, that they did not do it.

I cannot say that they had inhuman faces. They looked careworn; they perspired as if they had been chopping wood. Of course, it was their work. They themselves were subject to a hard discipline. If they had refused, it would have been done to them as they were doing it to others. "Lie down, begin!" the man with the lantern said to me. He had put the light on a rough table by the wall and looked at me with a kind of vulgar curiosity. I wanted to lie down, but something in me resisted. I would rather have been beaten standing up. It was terrible how difficult it was to force myself to lie down on the bed — a bed, often the comfort of a patient, the place for sleep, for death, for joy, for birth! How much I had to force myself not to beg for mercy from these people, who were simply doing their duty and could show me none! Now I understood what monstrous power the fear of bodily pain could exercise on a person. Toughening, stoic disdain for death does not count. Death cannot be scorned. Nor torture. "He is one of the smart ones," said one of the torturers scornfully, as he leafed through my papers while he held them close to the light of the lantern; "he is a doctor out of Zion, a wise man out of Zion." "Come on, hurry up, we have work to do; many are still waiting for us before we can go to sleep."

I lay there and clenched myself tightly with my hands. I wanted to hold my breath. At least I planned to. I lay so that they could not immediately strike the three bad ribs. I held my breath. But at the first dehumanizing blow I screamed out like an animal; I could hold nothing, not my breath, nothing. I wanted to protect my ribs. But when all the rest of my back had been beaten soundly and burned like fire, like hell, like searing, red-hot cuts, I rolled over so that the spot which had escaped them so far was exposed; and all three beat at it, in tempo, like threshers beating on the threshing floor, with all their force, breathing heavily; and they cried out in chorus: "Long live the wise ones from Zion." On "Zi" they struck — that is, one from the right, the other from the left, and the third wherever he could. Sweat ran down my face, tears from my eyes, blood from my lips. The skin of my body, however, did not bleed. They struck so skillfully that the skin did not burst anywhere. As they got tired, they struck some weaker blows, but they had turned the whips around so that they used the gristly end and held the thin end in their hands. They no longer struck only the upper part of my body but also my legs and the soles of my feet. It must have been fifty to sixty blows. I did not count them. The fourth man, the man with the lantern, the records, the author of the chorus of the wise man — he counted them.

I knew from my reading that a mature person cannot bear more than a hundred such blows. But before he dies from these blows he becomes unconscious. I did not. So they must have had the order to thrash me as hard as possible but to save my life.

I thought of the papers — if I thought of anything. I pressed my teeth together with such anger that they gnashed, and I thought that if they did not kill me I would still be master of *him*. He who succeeded in everything would not succeed in robbing me of my notes.

Then the pain burned even more strongly. I noticed that I vomited, and I felt very weak. Suddenly it was all dark.

But it was not death. The slaves had gone out and had left me in the dark. I had not heard the door open or close.

If I could just have had rest then! Don't they ever stop? I

thought. For the pain continued, my skin burned, I shook all over; I lay in the wetness, crushed. I held my ears shut, but I still heard the hissing of the horsewhip, the slap on the skin, the cries for help of the victim, the creaking of his bed on which he turned and twisted, the scornful cries — "Victorious world revolution" — and on the last syllable came the blow of the whip. In that way they gave themselves some variety in their work. They never did stop. I fell asleep hearing their choruses, their whips, our groaning and weeping. I slept. Deeply. That was a rarity, my comrades in misfortune told me. They did not know that I had thirteen sleepless nights in police headquarters behind me.

The next morning, as I hobbled from the barracks on my beaten legs and tried to breathe lightly because I had spit some blood during the night, I saw two of the slaves from the night before. They were people such as one sees every day, such as I had treated in great numbers in S. I had never recognized their real being, their nature; the frightful had remained hidden. If their Führer, their idol, their sweetly brutal idol, had not appeared one day, they would have continued as minor officials, factory workers, fishermen, foresters, peatcutters, noncommissioned officers. A living Satan had transformed them, and perhaps they did not understand themselves when after all this they returned to wife and child and beer. They ought not to be called bestial any more than someone mentally ill. That would be an injustice to animals. Maybe also to these torturers. They probably did not even have a feeling of infamy. They had no more conscience, no more reason in their behavior. The lowest in them had been called forth. I was beaten more and often, but the experience of the monster, grinding, crushing, consuming, of the first night never recurred. There were new trials, too. They did not want me to die. They remembered that I had served in the front lines in the war without being forced to. They inquired again and again for my records but without scorn. When they beat me, they did it simply and matter-of-factly, one, two, three. That was a mark of distinction. They were silent about Zion.

I felt wretched, but my resistance was not broken. There was a pause in my mistreatment. I was taken to a barracks for the sick, although others who were worse off stayed in the larger barracks and had to endure everything. A few days later the camp had a visitor — Helmut, who occupied a high rank in the SS and who was conducting a group of foreign journalists through the camp. We all had clean laundry, food was more abundant; we were not supposed to look like corpses on leave but to bring honor to the new Germany, the Third Reich, with its enlightened methods of education and its humanity. Helmut showed the foreigners everything — the electric plant, the crematorium in which the corpses were burned; the ashes were sent in soldered tin cans to the relatives with a bill for thirty-five marks. He showed them the kitchens with their exemplary cleanliness; he showed them several miserable, cowardly prisoners, who explained that the treatment was not at all bad and that they only wished to be released soon since they had learned better and had come to love the Führer with all their hearts. Helmut came with his staff to the hospital barracks. He saw me at once, as if he had known where I was lying. But not a muscle moved in his face; he made only a vague, circular gesture as if to say to the journalists: See, we have nothing to hide. We transform the Marxists, Democrats, Jews and Catholics into useful members of society. He was, of course, careful not to show them the camp arrangements: the horsewhips, or the minuscule dugout cells, in which one of us was imprisoned, standing up, for a half-day, for days, for weeks. To leave a person without light, in deadly loneliness, in suffocating heat, not able to take his own life, always standing until his knees are rubbed raw on the cement walls — is that not the best way to make him a good German? But I accustomed myself to ignore my indignation, thanks to my will power, since it would have embittered my life still more. I bore what I had to. One gets dull. The last remnant of hope is protected by this dullness, and it keeps one from lacerating oneself, for example, with remorse.

I thought that I would soon have to go back to the big barracks with its cots, endure the horsewhips, and take part in forced marches of fifteen to seventeen hours. But something seemed to have changed. Contrary to my expectations, I stayed in the hospital and was beaten no more; I was not subjected to torture, and nothing more was said of the papers. One night an SS man whose home was in my area came to me; he took me aside and told me that I had once saved his child, a boy of two years whom I no longer re-membered, and as thanks he wanted to give me some important information. Once every month the big dynamo in the central building was examined and oiled. For five minutes there was no light and the barbed wires lost their electricity. Well, that could be a trick of the camp command, which wanted to get rid of me in a simple fashion. Many prisoners were given the advice to commit suicide, and they were even provided with ropes. I would have the advantage of dying within a second by means of electricity, without the decision of suicide, and without long suffering from an unfortunate accident. On the other hand, it was also possible that my relatives — Heidi, Angelica, my father — had sought my release and had paid out much money, for money was always effective in the party, especially if it was a large amount. But I could not really believe it. So I wavered until evening. Then, however, the usual beatings, the cries of pain, arose from the barracks, and I said to myself that it would be better if I ventured it. In spite of all pre-cautions, more than one prisoner had succeeded in escaping. The barracks for the sick was less closely guarded than the others; who-ever was there was so near to the edge of the grave that he could not leave his bed by himself. I was by far the most healthy and strongest, and that made my decision easier. I knew that I could not stay there much longer. The guard made its round at eight o'clock. At about ten o'clock I got up, put on my clothes, and crept out to the barbed-wire fence. It was simple. If the light in the commandant's house and in the watchtower went out, there was a possibility that the barbed wire was no longer charged. I lay for hours, it seemed, with my stomach pressed on the grass covered with hoarfrost, and the screams of the poor tortured creatures did not stop in the winter night. As the clock in the commandant's house struck eleven, the light went out. It could be that it had gone out even earlier. In spite of the cold and the excitement, I had fallen asleep and had maybe missed a few minutes. But I wanted out. I threw myself, with all my force, with my back to the barbed wire in order to force the wires apart. They tore at my neck, my ears and my hands, but they yielded some to the pressure of my body and I could slip through. They were not alive. Other-wise I would have been dead, burned by electric shock. It was pitch-black. I had to feel my way through; I had to go through the wires with my head, holding my hands in front of my eyes. I did not dare bother about the pain. I was now entirely clear. I saw myself on a similar cold, clear, late winter night forcing myself through the barbed-wire jungle of the Western Front, and noticed how the intertwined wires, with their pointed spikes, clung to me, how they tore at me and wanted to hold me. I was outside with my head, and then it seemed to be impossible to go farther. At any moment the light, the current, could be turned on. With one last pull I tore myself through. With my hands clinging to the ground, I pulled my shoulders and body through. Then I was on the other side of the wires, with bleeding hands, forehead, neck, ears, knuckles.

I had to wait until the worst bleeding was over. Then, however, I noticed that I was so weak that my eyes fell shut. I lay down again, pressing my stomach into the grass. Then the light flared on. Scraps of my suit still clung to the wires. The breeze was cool, the stars shone clear. They seemed to be other stars, I thought, other air than inside in the camp. I forced myself up, took the first steps with effort; but gradually my strength returned and I went on, keeping myself carefully in the shadows.

The guard came by. I hid myself behind a tree. The sentry did not see me and went on, alternately whistling and dragging on his cigarette. I was surprised that he had not seen me. A somewhat experienced glance would surely have recognized a man even in the moonless night. The most difficult task was still before me. A thick wall of wooden stakes went around the camp. I had been a good gymnast, and for a healthy person it would not have been impossible to overcome such a barrier. But then I was much too weak, my heart pounded, blood dripped from my lips, and my poorly healed ribs hurt with every breath. My situation was much worse. I could not go back to the hospital barracks, for the barbed wire was charged. I went along the wall, completely calm and at the same time completely despairing.

I made the round, one kilometer to the left, one kilometer to the right. Suddenly I saw a little gate. Such entrances were for the guards. But what good did it do me if it were locked? But I thought of my lack of faith in Berne. I shook the door. Then the great miracle occurred — for the first time in my life, when I was least expecting it, it was revealed — the door yielded. I was out of the camp. Was I saved? Not really!

I knew where the camp was — about five hours from S. Of course, I had to avoid the main roads. In fact, it was better to go at night and to hide in the daytime. Even then the danger was great that they would catch me and either beat me to death at once with their gun butts or torture me to death in the camp to give the other prisoners a frightening example.

I therefore did not get to my neighborhood that night. On the morning of the second day I became so hungry that I chewed birchbark, dried grasses and ferns. Here and there was a little snow. That quenched my thirst. But my strength did not diminish as fast as I had feared. Finally, in the gray dawn, I saw the moor ahead of me. I came out of the woods where the little electric plant was located and where there was some light. The motor hummed. It smelled of moss, gasoline, and oil. Should I enter and ask the mechanic for a piece of bread, for shelter? I heard him go back and forth in the stone shed, and the smell of freshly brewed coffee gave me great pain. I controlled myself, however, and went on. The poor peatcutters had been among the first and most enthusiastic followers of A.H.; as a boy I had often seen their shacks covered with tarpaper when I was wandering in the moor. They knew me as a doctor. I had helped an old woman there. I continued on my way to them. They took me in when I knocked. They must have suspected from where I came, for in all likelihood the entire neighborhood knew where I had been taken. At first they acted as if I had come on a sick call and spoke quite freely with me.

Somewhat later I understood what had been involved in my less than miraculous escape from the concentration camp. But the peatcutters were not involved. They had not forgotten the doctor. They accepted the danger of being sent to the camp for an indefinite time when they put me in the master's bed, which was still warm, and let me sleep, when they fed me, when they provided me with everyday clothes and accompanied me the next evening to S. I had planned to see my father and Angelica and ask for more help. But my father's house was dark and forsaken. I did not see my children.

The peatcutters waited outside. They were not surprised by my misfortune. They took me back with them on the narrow paths through the bare moors past the Oster Lakes, frozen over. We sat down by a peat fire in the hut, drank coffee, ate bread, and discussed everything quietly. At night we started out, and they guided me on little paths over the mountains to the Austrian border. They were willing to risk their lives and their freedom, and they did. I had told them everything. They helped me but they did not pity me. They could give me no money, really. All that I received was a silver mark. It was touching that they said (it was a father and his son) that they had to be grateful, that they had owed me the money for more than a year for my helping the old woman.

In the Austrian hamlet beyond the border there was no post office. I had to go farther into the country, always afraid that I would meet an Austrian policeman who would ask me for my papers. Finally I came to a larger village. I went to the post office, sent a telegram to my wife in Berne, and paid for it with the silver mark. I told her where I was. My writing was awkward; I stuttered; the many tortures had hurt my voice, and the loss of blood, the long walk, and the hunger had taken their toll. I needed a long time to comprehend that I was really no longer in the camp. Two days later my wife came and released me from the village inn, where they had taken me on faith, without a cent of money and with torn clothes. They suspected, of course, that I was a fugitive; they could see the scars and welts on my face and hands. They lent me clothes: an overcoat, a rough but clean shirt. They were good people. But what was incomprehensible to me was that here, too, they loved A.H. They longed for his coming. They wanted to live under his rule. They saw me and must have realized my fate. But on the other hand, in their fanatic belief in A.H. they did not see it. It made me almost despair as I came to understand how unteachable people are. But I too was still not at the end; I had given my wife too much credit, or I had seen in her something that was not there, and a bitter revelation awaited me.

After a few days of recuperation we rode into Switzerland. It seemed strange that my wife had brought with her our common passport, which the police had taken from me in M. She had all the keys, even the one to the safe deposit box in the bank in Basel. I wanted to go to the bank on our way, but my wife said that

I ought to go home first, that is, to Berne. My children were waiting there for me. That was a lie, and a poor one. Victoria had learned to lie no better than I. The children were with my father and Heidi in M. Their life in S. had been made impossible because they were half-Jewish, even though they were the children of a respected doctor and the grandchildren of a much beloved wood manufacturer of "German blood." In a large city it was easier to disappear. My father, Heidi, and Angelica had made the sacrifice. Therefore I had found my father's villa empty. Why had she wanted to get me out of Basel so quickly? I asked, shortly before we entered the hotel, when she would have to admit to her lie about the children. Because presumably Basel swarmed with spies and German secret agents, and I would be better situated in Berne.

I waited only a few days before preparing to go to Basel to get the papers out of the bank. My wife hindered me with a thousand excuses. The child that she had been carrying at the time of my departure to Switzerland, almost a year before, had been lost through a miscarriage. She did not feel well. Since she began to weep at the least provocation, I did not ask why I should not go.

She had other secrets, too. She met people whom I did not know and did not like. She had money to spend; I knew nothing of its origin. At first I thought that she had attached herself to another man. Why should I, who understood so much, not understand that, too? Had I not been as if dead, without any prospect of ever again being free? Did I have a right to stop her if she wanted to spend the rest of her life with another man, perhaps one of her own race? I would have forgiven her for that — in fact, I would have helped her as much as possible if she had confessed something like that to me. In my delusion, I was at the point of offering her the divorce which she had suggested to me a year before.

She wept; it was her only method of answering me — in that she was like my mother. Finally I took the safe deposit box key secretly off her key ring, went to Basel, and opened the safe. The papers were gone. Only some banknotes and many newspaper clippings fastened together, I don't know anymore from what papers or about what event. I returned home in a stupor after I had convinced myself that it was really my box that had been robbed. My wife was waiting for me at the station. This time she did not cry.

She told me the truth. Helmut had gotten in touch with her. The only way I could be rescued was by the release of the papers. My later experiences in the camp had been a put-up job. The electricity had been deliberately cut off. The sentry had deliberately closed both eyes. Was it not good? Had I not been saved? "I lost my first husband because of his own fault," she responded in a cold voice to my protests; "I had no children by him and I recovered. You did not have the right to do what you did. You behaved badly. I did right. We will have the children come here or to Paris, and you will be happy that everything has gone like this."

She was right, but I was not happy.

PART IV

W E DID NOT LEAVE Switzerland for Paris until the spring of 1934. I was a sick man. I had not recovered from the ill treatment. If I spoke loudly or moved vigorously, the pain in my chest was almost unbearable. Victoria spared me. But this troubled me. I would have liked it best not to see anyone for days on end. I had to endure her, for she was the only one who bound me to life. But both of us felt that too much had been destroyed between us. I had become shy. I never looked anyone in the eye, I was afraid of people – of all people, and therefore also of her. I looked around, full of fear, each time before I spoke. Was I still afraid that I could be overheard? And the worst part was that I did not trust Victoria anymore. One can live very well for years with someone without love; I had experienced that in the years before the war in the case of Angelica. But one cannot live without trust. My wife had to notice it. But instead of understanding me, she too became distrustful. I did not trust her because, by giving the papers to the Secret State Police, she had stamped my entire sacrifice as a useless attempt of resistance against A.H. I had had a weapon against him, perhaps only a tiny one, but it had been important to me, and I had been able to endure the tortures in the camp only with the thought that at that point, in spite of all his brutal power, I was superior to him, and in the feeling of love and trust for my wife. He had the papers: I no longer had my wife, for after this first betrayal, I believed her to be capable of another. She began to distrust me because she did not understand my behavior and saw hatred of the Jews in it.

She was reminded and reminded me inopportunely of my mother's hatred of the Jews, of her ingratitude after the trial, of the angry words which my mother had screamed at her through the crack in the door, of the promise I had made at her deathbed that I would not marry Victoria.

All these facts were true. But the lies, as A.H. had poured them in a monstrous stream over the country, made people happy in their deluded intoxication. Our truths, which we whispered to each other in long, sleepless nights in order not to disturb the neighbors, made us unhappy and estranged us still more. A.H.'s lies had united the Germans from the North Sea to the Bavarian mountains, had torn down all boundaries. And we in our little hotel room in Berne could find nothing to bring us closer together.

I had been able to attack or shun my mother as long as she lived and to be on Victoria's side. After she died, however, she had become a saint to me. I had been Victoria's husband for almost twelve years, but I had been my mother's son from the beginning of my life.

My wife was still attractive, a mature, somewhat voluptuous beauty, but I did not see her aging. I wanted to draw her closer, but she retreated imperceptibly; she whispered that I had to spare myself. She was right. I was wrong. My back was a single wound which healed badly, and yet I would have preferred a thousand times to awaken with pain in the morning rather than our lying next to each other like two stone columns.

Sometimes we took pleasant walks and crossed a splendid bridge. From there one could see the entire city and the beautiful mountains and the ice-covered peaks, especially the immensity of the Jungfrau. And again my wife put her hand warmly in my arm and whispered in my ear, her soft, silky hair, with only an occasional trace of gray, touching my cheek, "Aren't you grateful to me that I got you out of that horrible country and camp? Don't think that it was easy! Helmut hates Jewesses, and it took me a long time, until . . ." I shook my head. I was furious that she reminded me of it, that I was indebted to her, and that she had sacrificed something of her pride to secure from Helmut that for which he was obligated to me as a friend. She noticed it, took her arm out of mine and, blushing with shame and anger, could not keep from cutting me to the quick: "On the wooden bed and under the horsewhips, you would have spoken differently! You would not have been ashamed of me there! But you know that I did not force you into marriage. I could have lived alone; my father often advised me not to trust you."

This was an untruth. But I let it go. I hoped for nothing and looked forward to nothing. I read the newspapers with their frightful reports as if I were leafing through a lexicon which translated a language unknown to me, for example, Chinese, into another unknown, perhaps Japanese. There were words, sounds, rasps, vowels, and breaths. My soul was not in it.

Even my children were strangers to me. If I had only been able to see them in S.! Their letters came; I did not open them and left them for my wife, who took them with fear and passion and read them over and over. I did not ask what was in them. I began to study French again; I wanted to be able to speak it a little when I got to Paris. My wife spoke it very well. We conversed in French. And just as years before, in the case of Angelica, this conversation in a foreign tongue estranged us more than anything else. I noticed it with silent joy. I made progress. I stopped loving and began to speak fluently.

At the end of March we arrived in Paris and moved into a small hotel in Montmartre. I could not bear to stay inside. During the first weeks I wandered around in the streets from early morning to late evening. But I saw nothing. I was blind to everything except the one thought — to find peace. But how could I find peace when I hated so strongly, when I became more and more lonely, when everything slid off me, when I had no activity? It is a burden for a growing person to live without work, even when his sustenance is provided. My wife, who had become very independent, had brought a modest sum along from Basel. After a time it seemed to me that it must be almost gone, and as much as I disliked discussing money with her, I did raise the question. She smiled, showed all her lovely teeth, and touched a small bouquet of violets, still damp, which she wore in the low neck of her dress. She seemed to be unconcerned about money.

Her mood changed. Sometimes she endured being without news from the children for three days without complaining and worrying, but she controlled herself better than I did. We both hated the Third Reich. But she hated it because Jews suffered so much there, and I hated it because it had turned my people into cringing, obedient slaves who were satisfied in their state of slavery. Actually, we could have come to an understanding in our hate, could have made our life easier, but we grew more and more estranged with each day, and sometimes I thought that my wife began to hate the non-

Jew in me and to regret her marriage. I did not repay her in kind. I looked away when one of her cold, boring, green-blue glances wanted to strike me. I say it again — I wanted only peace.

Soon I realized that I would not find it without some regular activity. What should I begin? I could not think about being a doctor again, for the laws of the land to which I had to be grateful for hospitality forbade it; the native doctors had banded together and created a law against refugee doctors. We could not even participate in the medical seminars. Except for a few of us, we had to forget what we had been.

Perhaps there might have been an opportunity here or there. But my profession repulsed me now. I could see no blood; bare skin which reminded me of the torture scenes in the concentration camp nauseated me; and, I must admit it openly, everyone nauseated me.

I learned that doctors were needed at the Pasteur Institute. There they carried on massive scientific investigations — breeding bacillae and experimenting with animals in order to clarify purely scientific questions or to find new cures. I went to the gate of the institute. I thought that perhaps under the direction of experienced, humane scholars I could find a new purpose in life. But before I stepped through the gate, the old choking aversion rose up in me. I began to tremble, I lost my breath — all was dark before me. All from aversion, not weakness. I could not do anything to an animal; I could no longer comprehend that the suffering or painful death of an animal meant nothing if it served pure science or brought new cures for the combatting of people's ills. I no longer saw in human life, as before the war, the highest value of life. It had become something cheap. It was worth nothing.

One evening I said to myself that I too had become valueless. It was immaterial if I lived a few more years or not. And whom did I blame silently but bitterly for that? My wife, who had destroyed my last faith and loyalty in a person. In the evenings, we sat silently opposite each other in the larger of the two rooms. She had bought a chessboard, and we played, seemingly quietly, play after play. But even in the game, in the silent being together, hatred broke through from the depths. We played with bitterness, we invented stratagems and tricks in order to win. Never had we both played so brilliantly. Maybe hatred makes for ingenuity. Afterward we stood up unwillingly, with distorted faces and burning eyes, clutching the last figures in our hands, for neither of us wanted to accept defeat, neither wanted to go to sleep as the loser. There too I found no peace.

In the early summer months I stopped my wanderings through the streets, museums and churches. It was pointless; I could just as well have been wandering aimlessly behind the electrically charged barbed wire of the camp. I sought peace, but I did not find it in the beauties and rarities of the museum. I had separated myself somewhat from my wife; we did not kiss each other any-more, and we had stopped playing chess. I held myself aloof from the period by avoiding contacts with other refugees, outcasts, those who knew no peace. I stopped reading the newspaper. I looked for some manual labor and found it with difficulty. It was — wash-ing dishes in an emigrant kitchen. It was not the roomy, tiled, underground story of the Prince Regent of Bavaria. The vile smells, the ingredients often spoiled, the rancid fat, the poor crockery, should have disgusted me more than everything in the Prince Regent. But that was not the case. The hard work from noon to three o'clock, and evenings from seven to ten o'clock, was good for me. I was delighted about the few francs which it paid, which I accepted greedily. I did not tell my wife what I was doing or how much I earned.

After a few weeks I gave up this work. I could not endure the nearness of my fellow sufferers. I wanted to forget Germany and not always be reminded of it.

In the summer of 1934 Captain R. was murdered, along with several hundred other men and women. Without accusation, with-out trial, without a record.

R. had always been a strong man. He was intelligent and had a clear eye. Otherwise, how could he have risen from an instruc-tional officer in the Bolivian army in 1925 to be master of three million people in 1934 who served him blindly, and through him the topmost Führer? But he was so unaware of A.H.'s nature that he trusted him like a brother. What A.H. did was no uncontrolled burst of rage. It was carefully thought out and followed step by step to its end. He had enriched himself by R.'s energy, but he had been cold, calculating, superior. He did not love. He had never loved; therefore he never lost his predominance. Blood was like water to him.

What he hated and feared in R. and his circle has never really been clear. They were too important in the world — that is certain. A.H. had to be alone. One night A.H. went to R., awakened him, arrested him, spit at him, maligned him, put him in chains. The shoulder patches were torn from his uniform and from those of his young friends. The Führer is supposed to have beaten the adjutant of the chief of staff, a Count Spr., with his famous whip. R. was granted the privilege, which I knew well from the camp, of ending his life by suicide. R. was a great soldier; therefore he could die by means of an honorable bullet. He had been given a heavy revolver with a smile. He refused. Not out of cowardice — R. was one of the bravest men of his time — but out of servile love for A.H. He begged A.H. to shoot him himself. But A.H. could not do that. He was a gentle person. He never spilled blood. He left R.'s cell and told a few SS people to do what was necessary. I read these reports coldly. I had known R. I had never loved him or respected him. Perhaps I had feared him and that had attracted me. . . . He and I had scarcely spoken to each other. What was I to him? What was he to me? But R. meant much to A.H., and for R., A.H. was simply God on earth!

R. and his followers were not the only ones who had fallen. A week later A.H. listed in a great speech seventy-seven names. It could also have been two hundred and seventy or eight hundred and seventy. Finally everyone agreed on three hundred and seventy. One did not puzzle long. Since the war, human life was no longer valuable. There may have been some in the group who were less guilty, or even some who were completely innocent. A.H. conceded that "a number of deeds of violence, which have no connection with this action, will be referred to the normal courts for judgment." Lie, fantasy. No one ever heard later of such an activity of the normal court. Dead was dead.

Had the three million SA men mutinied, and in order to break the mutiny, had these three hundred and seventy been sacrificed?

A.H. presented himself to the judgment of the nation in a great address: "Mutinies are broken according to eternally accepted laws. In this hour I was responsible for the fate of the German nation, and therefore I was the highest judge of the German people in these twenty-four hours." But was R., the most loyal of the loyal, a mutineer? Had he not been devoted in all quietness to the joys of his existence as he understood them? Had he not been awakened out of sleep? Does a mutineer sleep so soundly? A Judas who betrays his friend — does he cling so to the savior, seeking death from his hand? But the idol of the German people was not satisfied with such an accusation. A.H. betrayed those who had served him, whom he himself had made into powerful assistant commanders in chief, subdictators, to whom he entrusted the greatest authority and responsibility. Blazing with wrath, he screamed something about immorality and corruption; their life had become evil. He called them conspirators, instigators, accused them of living luxuriously from the coins of our poorest fellow citizens; he reproached them with homosexuality, which he had known for years. "I want to see men as SA leaders, not silly monkeys." He implicated the French ambassador. When the latter objected to the lie, A.H. acted as if nothing had happened; he was pleasant, and nothing more was said. Murder had been committed; there had been no attempt at even a semblance of a trial. General von Schleicher,* an earlier imperial chancellor, was murdered. Perhaps they were afraid that he had records dating back to A.H.'s war experiences. His wife was also murdered; she certainly possessed no records. The aged Bavarian ex-minister von Kahr was murdered in revenge for his action eleven years earlier. People were shot down at the prison walls because they had the same name as one of the guilty.

But that was not what revolted me to the point of suffocation. The old imperial president telegraphed: "From the reports given me, I see that you have smothered all high treasonable plots in the germ by your decisive action and your brave personal intervention. I extend to you my deeply felt thanks and my sincere appreciation." A Protestant bishop said in a service that it was the duty of all

* General von Schleicher was Chancellor of Germany, 1932–1933.

Germans to thank God for this salvation: "We want to stand behind him, interceding that God may protect him further and grant him strength and success in his great work." The worst for me was to see how he was really loved now, when all "German blood" trembled for him, voluptuously yielded to him. He had made all Germans into Angelicas. No one objected. No one of the many who were still in a position to do so refused to breathe the air of that land of slavery and emigrate.

Germany stank of murder and treachery, and everyone breathed in the stink as if it were the fragrance of roses. For several days I did not go home. I was ashamed to face my wife, to admit that I was a German and that I could not exchange my blood for another. But then I was ashamed of that thought too. Was blood what mattered? Had I become A.H.'s slave, too, in spirit? Never have I been so close to suicide as at that time. Only the thought that I would then surrender to him of my own free will held me back, not the thought of wife, father, children.

The lists of those executed in the mass murders which appeared in the German newspapers must have been inaccurate and incomplete. I looked through them and found the name H. von Kaiser. I remained calm. I was surprised at how little I felt. I reasoned logically that only the elder Kaiser, who had lived for years in Italy, had been ennobled — his son had no right to the "von." And what could H. not signify? I remembered the scorn with which Helmut's father had pointed out the name O. Schwarz years before. I knew that I owed my life to Helmut. But what was there to be grateful for? Could I give thanks for such an existence? It was empty, cold and more troubled than existence in the camp and in flight.

My wife was more upset by the report. She cried, she tore her hair, she screamed so loud that I had to hold her mouth shut, for I did not want to have the others in the little hotel complain about us because of disturbances every night. Should I consider that perhaps she felt something deeper for Helmut, as ugly — and as anti-Semitic — as he was? Even this thought did not disturb me. As an eyewitness I noticed that Victoria, weeping and throwing herself about in an armchair, had worn-out soles. For some time she had been more economical. So I asked her, partly to divert her to something else, if we were really in desperate straits. "Yes, yes," she said, "we are," and added that it was not only we, two elderly people, who were lost in any case, but the children – they were in need and did not even know it. She started to weep again. I left and closed the door quietly behind me. The next day she asked me to forgive her, that I would soon understand everything. I looked at her questioningly. She did not want to say more. She did not want to lie, but neither could she tell the whole truth. We went together to a cobbler, sat down on chairs, took off our very dilapidated shoes (for mine were no better than hers), and waited patiently until it was our turn. A crowd of other people waited – the men in socks and the women in coarsely mended, washed-out, synthetic silk stockings – until they got their mended shoes back. They took out their wallets, counted the French money; they moved their lips, and I saw that they were figuring in German whether the money would suffice.

We had to wait less than three hours. We emigrants were all accustomed to waiting. When we were on the street again, my wife said that she felt more courageous and stable as soon as she had good thick soles under her feet. I believed her, for her walk, which had become quite dragging and reminded me of the shuffling walk of her father, was again as light as that of the young girl who ran up the steps with chessboard and clattering figures to play chess with my father and me. At home I ran my hand very lightly over her hair. She quivered; even this slight caress seemed to disturb her. Only very slowly did we begin to move nearer to each other, and I thought it impossible that we would ever love each other as we had at the beginning of our marriage or even in the last years in S.

Two days later Helmut came to us. He had been wounded – he did not say where or how; he carried his left arm in a sling, which was very soiled from the journey. He looked old and decayed. He shook hands with both of us somewhat self-consciously. We offered him the best chair, brought him some food, and watched him as he ate and then washed himself. He did it so awkwardly because of his wounded arm that my wife laughingly washed his face and neck and hands with my sponge. He did not say anything about his experiences – not a word about how he had fled from Germany. I showed him his name on the list. He shrugged his shoulders;

probably his thoughts were somewhere else. He had no French money except for a few small coins, but he did have a traveler's letter of credit for several hundred francs. He asked me to go to the bank immediately and collect the money for him. I objected that they would not hand it over to me; he would certainly have to give me at least some identification. "You?" he asked laconically. He looked at my wife, and she motioned that I should go. I was scarcely out the door when I heard their first words, spoken in such a passionate tone as I had not heard her use since we left S. "And Bobby?" He moved his chair closer to her; I heard his steps on the uncarpeted floor. He spoke so quickly that I could not follow him and I did not want to. I went. Contrary to my expectation, I got the money. I allowed myself the luxury of buying a bottle of good wine and flowers from this money and brought them to my wife and to him. They paid no attention. They sat opposite each other, playing chess with determined expressions. I watched their plays. Sometimes I could have helped him, who was a stronger but more incautious player; sometimes her, who played only very routinely and was really losing. I had always had the desire to interfere on the side of the weaker players, to give advice, perhaps with a glance, to play fate.

Since my imprisonment, I had been driven even more decidedly to the side of the weaker. There, however, it was only play for the sake of play. I controlled myself and let the game take its own course.

In the evening Helmut settled down in my room. His cheeks were still hot, and his pulse beat rapidly. He asked me half in jest, half in earnest, if I did not want to change the bandage quickly, look at his wound, treat him as his oldest, his only friend? Was it sport, was it serious? I acted as if it were a joke and said that foreign doctors were prohibited from practicing here. But I would take him the next morning to a French clinic where those without means were treated free and where everything was done in the most modern way.

We undressed in the dark; only when I was almost asleep did I remember that we had not said good-night to each other.

I really should have been grateful to Helmut for coming. His presence quieted me. Something of earlier times, of the time before the war, had returned with him, and I slept better that night than in all the previous time. My back was still sore in spots, there where the welts crossed. I had to sleep on my stomach, and then I had too little air. That night I had enough air as well as no pains in the scars from the horsewhips. I got up before him; I was ashamed to wash myself in his presence and force on him the sight of my miserable body. But had it been any better for him? He had been silent about his experiences of June 30. As I came back from my wife's room, he was standing at the washstand. I had not knocked; I had thought, what was the need between two lifelong friends? He was startled by the sound of the door closing, dived instinctively like a wild animal into his rumpled bed (he had obviously slept more restlessly than I), and pulled a huge automatic pistol from under his pillow. He could handle it only with his right hand, for his left was encumbered with the bandage. I laughed; he stopped short. I had no fear of huge pistols, but I was afraid of the de-humanized, really bestial, hunted expression on his pale, ugly face. He forced himself to laugh and acted as if everything had been a joke and theatrical. I forced myself to approach him, took the heavy weapon out of his hand, and put it under the pillow again. Another one was there — hard, smooth, cool — a little revolver inlaid with silver. As if the automatic pistol were not enough! I helped him dress and then left him alone since he wanted that. He refused to let me take him to the clinic. We did not see each other until evening. I had assumed that he would look for another lodging, but he did not want to leave us — for fear of pursuers, I thought, for something timid remained in his face. My wife, too, was restless, I knew, because of the children.

We sat around the table, and they began to talk about money matters. They mentioned names which I heard for the first time, perhaps intermediaries with whose help my wife had received reports about the children. I did not know. Really, it was senseless, for emigrants were not forbidden to have correspondence with their children. Of course, she may have been afraid that it would harm them if they received letters from Paris. Helmut smiled sadly; suddenly he turned to me as if he saw me for the first time, took my hand, and asked me with his youthful smile whether we did not want to write a begging letter to the old man in Rome. I knew that he had had several hundred francs the day before. How could he have spent them in the meantime? But he gave no explanation; his face was again fixed and rejecting, and it did not brighten even when I, together with my wife, composed a long letter to his father. I wanted to make it brief. That had always been most effective with the old man. Helmut, however, suggested sentimental phrases, basically cold (he wrote as A.H. spoke), and my wife was on his side. The answer did not come for several weeks. He refused to send money; he would receive his son if it were necessary because Katinka had spoken in his favor. (Why did he still act like her slave? Did it help him?) Only at the end did he speak of me; a man like me did not need him — I would fight my way through as always, and he would come to see me again before his death, that is, before the beginning of winter.

I did not like his words, but I was silent about them. When Helmut and Victoria berated the old man for his niggardliness — after all, he could not take his money to the grave — I was silent. He was really my father. If he thought of death, he knew why. The thought of losing him touched me more than any fear that my own father might die someday. It is probably not right to feel that way about one's own blood, but I would have preferred to have him there a thousand times more than my children, who were to come to us accompanied by my father and Heidi. The only good about that was that Helmut freed me of his constant presence. He found another room, and I did not need to leave my room and wander the streets when he received mysterious company, either very military or very delicate gentlemen.

He kept his own secrets; I kept mine. One day he did begin to speak about matters to which there had been passing references — that he had paid for my rescue with a kind of disgrace. To be sure, he had given the notes which I had put into the safe deposit box — down to the last sheet — to the Secret State Police, but not even they were received with favor. The most important part was supposed to be missing, that is, the part concerning relationships with women. It is true that in the long conversation in P. I had discovered much that has been kept from public knowledge. But even in 1918 I had not written a word of that.

I still know it all. It is a case of too great importance. But you will look in vain for anything here. This secret, too, I wrote down in hieroglyphics which no one but me can decipher. The big man could not believe that, and he regretted that he had let me slip out of his grasp alive. However, it may also be that he was afraid to kill someone who had restored his vision by a miracle. Could not a second miracle make him blind again, if he were to extinguish my light as he had so many others?

Paris was beautiful, heavenly, wonderful; it spilled over with life. The old and revered mixed magically with the modern and daring. But was it there for me? Was it there for us? It was not our language. I had known the language since my student days, but never succeeded in learning it so well that I could speak without mistakes.

It was impossible for those like us to disappear among the four million. The German language, in which we thought, hoped, feared, calculated, remembered, and dreamed (was it not our whole life, all that remained to us?), was really a forbidden language, something which no longer belonged to us and which should have become foreign to us. But it was not! My wife could not grasp that. She had revived again at the thought of having the children with us. She sang sometimes, ran lightfootedly up the many steps, embraced me and kissed me again and again. Not like her husband, more like her child. I stroked her hair and forced myself to do so with a steady hand so that she would not see how I was trembling.

At night we had intercourse. For her it seemed natural; to me it was grueling. I did it for her sake, and acted as if I had longed for her, so that she would have to believe that she would have failed me otherwise. I began searching for work. I knew that there were different committees which granted sizable sums to the poorest emigrants. I sent my wife, although I was now the one who looked more needy than she, a well-preserved woman in her best years.

I did not want to accept charity but I had to. Something in me rebelled. As a young man I had lived with Kaiser's help, but at that time I could hope to pay off all of it; I no longer had that hope, for I experienced every day as if it were my last. Shortly before the arrival of my children I exerted myself. "Make an end of it," I said to myself, sitting on a bench in the beautiful Luxembourg gardens which were already beginning to show the breath of autumn, in front of me the little reservoir in which children let their boats sail. "End it all! You can find a way to do that; your wife will get along with the children with the help of the committees and perhaps Helmut; Kaiser will give her what he has refused you because he overestimates you. Good! But if you want to continue to live, don't harass yourself anymore. Forget or die! Doubt is good. Living is also good. But living and doubting together are not good."

Beautiful principles! In any case it was good for me that I attacked myself roughly. I did not feel so sorry for myself on the way home and found the courage to expose myself to the jokes of my comrades in misery in the emigrant kitchen and to beg for work, which they gave me out of sympathy and at poorer rates than in the spring — that is, no more payment of a few francs per day but only free food. I said nothing at home. I was ashamed.

My parents came. My stepmother was now just as familiar and just as strange as my old, distinguished-looking father, who planned to greet me at first with the "German salute" but let his outstretched arm fall. My children embraced me but then rubbed their cheeks and their lips, for my cheeks were prickly. I laughed; I had done the same as a child.

Something else really touched me. Heidi had brought a whole loaf of peasant bread along. When I took it up like a little child and felt it, my forsaken home came to mind. I put the bread down and dashed out to the street, where I walked up and down a quiet side street, sobbing, crying, holding my teeth together, my hands pressed over my eyes until I became calm.

The next day I showed my parents the sights; I excused myself at mealtime — I had an important business engagement — and went to wash plates; the same in the evening. Heidi was deceived; my father was not. He told me when I came home late in the evening, dead tired, that he understood. There was not much that he could do for me in the Third Reich, but each month he would send me thirty marks. Every German could send ten marks to relatives abroad; so he, Heidi, and Angelica — it was only a drop. I was grateful; my eyes, however, stayed dry.

My wife did not want to tell the children that they had to stay here. She wanted to wait until my parents had gone. I insisted, however, that she should tell the truth at once. I believed that one had to be born a liar. I had seldom lied, and when I did, I always created mischief; God's blessing did not rest on my lies. My wife looked at me somewhat unwillingly with her aquamarine eyes; then she laughed and romped around the room so that she not only wakened the children but also our sensitive neighbors. The next morning I took my son aside and told him everything. He grew pale. I asked him if he would be responsible for telling his sister. Being entrusted with this responsibility lightened the matter for him. The children had not anticipated this. They did not find the city beautiful. They made invidious comparisons, for example, about the dirt in the streets or in the subway, about the bread, the water. Everything that was different from the way it was at home seemed "funny" to them, and I saw with bitterness how much they loved their city, their home, which had become so foreign to me.

My parents left. They gave us their travel accessories: brushes, combs, blankets, and so on. They had soon realized how much we needed these things. The children, on the other hand, were totally lacking in understanding. They always used the German *Heil* as a greeting. The hotel porter showed his wry, sour smile. On the street they deliberately spoke German very loudly. My wife tried to teach them a little French so that they could go for milk or bread. They did not want to learn anything; they held their ears shut and screamed nonsense.

My wife had never possessed patience to any degree. I took her aside and left the children alone; they calmed down quickly and even apologized to her, and were willing to copy the few phrases, which they did, chewing the end of the pen holder with their beautiful white teeth.

The children could not write in Latin script, or acted as if they could not. My wife let it pass for one or two days; on the third she lost her patience. I would have liked to absent myself from those scenes; I controlled myself only with effort, but I saw that she was the weaker. I had to support her against the two ill-bred brats.

If they had been only ill bred! But they had been too well reared — that is, in *his* spirit. My anger almost overpowered me when I saw that *his* spirit was also in these half-Jewish children, that my children considered themselves three-quarters German and only one-quarter Jewish (perhaps this was Angelica's work, teaching

187

them this stupid calculation as a revenge), that they praised their Führer and sang his songs, marching in step around the room, and that they lauded "German blood." But did I dare yield to my anger? Everyone else could do it before I would. Everything was almost lost when Victoria, in her great sensitivity about everything which pertained to Jews, and in her boundless disillusionment about the children who had returned to her so changed, came to the end of her self-control and dashed at them to punish them. Even in anger she had a light hand. She herself had never been struck; the Kaiser-Jew spurned paddling as a method of rearing. I think she would never have hurt the children on purpose. But she was overcome — with a distorted face and burning eyes she threw herself at the children. Instead of creeping, each into a different corner, or running away, they held each other and tried to protect each other, both screaming violently. Suddenly I recognized in this screaming of my children my own voice, as I lay under the horsewhip. I had been beaten inhumanely without cause; they were threatened by a harmless punishment. I later learned that they had endured much more painful punishments in their school. And yet I have to admit it, to my shame, I regretted then that I had regained my courage shortly before at the Luxembourg pond and had not put an end to my life in the Seine flowing nearby.

I did the necessary, however. I threw myself in front of the children and received the few blows and thumps from Victoria's little fists and laughed out of a full heart. I laughed as she wanted to scratch my face with her nails. I laughed as the children called as out of one mouth: "Help us; we don't have to accept anything from a Jewess. Help! Help!" I laughed when my wife in her senseless anger screamed that she could see whom I preferred; she did not want to stay any longer under the same roof with a Jew-hater, and she "did not recognize her children anymore." I laughed, since I remembered the same words which my blessed mother had cried out. I laughed at the children, who were completely astonished at the really comical turn this German battle in a French hotel room had assumed.

But I also knew the way to heal my son. "You are really a brave little fellow?" I said to him questioningly as his late grandfather had once asked me. But I did not ask the question in order to toughen him against "pain and suffering" and to make him into a Spartan, but to bring him by visual means, the direct method of illustrative teaching, to the point of respecting pain. He should begin to despise those who in their brutality demean helpless people lower than an animal by torture. I knew well that the Führer in all his sentimentality had made decrees protecting animals — consideration for dogs, no more kosher killing of cattle, humane treatment of animals. How much that had influenced the naïve spirit of Robert and Lise and many other millions of children! I pulled my son into the next room, locked the door, and undressed.

I showed him, turning slowly in a circle, my back, my thighs, my legs down to my heels. I took his hand to let him feel the welts, still damp, which swelled up red and thick each time I was excited or disturbed. I did not say, "This is what they did to your father." I did not say, "Your father is . . ." It was enough. He burst into tears. I told him not to cry. "Crying is forbidden!" He should wash his hands and face, go back to his mother and sister, and do his duty. He did it. He staggered a little in walking, the sturdy, strong boy with his quarter of Jewish blood, but he had always been energetic, just as I had been as a child. He asked his mother's pardon. He took his sister aside. After that they were more amenable. No more German salutes. They no longer poked fun at this beautiful country. But it took them a long time to learn to write the Latin letters.

They did not learn to write French until much later, and as far as I could judge they never wrote it without mistakes. But they soon spoke it fluently; Lise spoke it best, then Bobby, then my wife, and finally I. I had the largest vocabulary and made the finest distinctions, but I also had the poorest enunciation. I tried very hard to improve, but I never succeeded.

We had taken on a great responsibility when we had the children come. I did not know how much money my wife possessed or whether the chief source, remittances from Helmut, had now stopped. I wanted to know, for I was still the head of the family. One evening, when I came home late, I asked my wife to come with me to a little café on the corner. She got out of bed, put something on, laid more covering on Lise, who slept in the same room with her, and we went. I told my wife on the steps going down what my income was. The stairway was long, the list short. It was still only thirty marks a month.

The franc had decreased in value, so that thirty marks could buy much more in Paris than at home. But it was still beggarly. We had not yet reached the entrance of the hotel when my wife asked me quietly, but emphasizing every syllable, "And why are you not working?" I said that it was not possible to get a work permit as a doctor here, the law did not allow it. "Others don't pay any attention," she said. "You must realize that you let the children come and we must think of the future."

"What should I do?" I asked.

"You are the man, you must know, she said, and took my arm.

"I don't know."

"I often advised you and not always badly. If you had followed my advice, we would still be at home and the children would have a roof over their heads."

"What is done is done," I said, and tried to deflect her, for I was not interested in disturbing the past.

She continued more gently while she withdrew her arm from mine, which pleased me. "I don't want to say that I took the papers out of the safe only on your account. It was also on my account. It was also on account of the children. In fact, it was even for the sake of your father, as strange as that may seem to you. But you are right, it is not necessary to speak about it. I have not made many mistakes in my life, but these were serious. I should never have married Leon Lazarus. I should never have waited so long for you!"

"*You* waited for me?" I asked. She was silent and then she said with her old clear laugh,

"What a child you are!"

I shook my head but laughed too.

"I have to care for all three of you like a mother, but I will succeed. I led and advised my father, too; he never moved a step without me. Now we must decide how we can rear the children to be good and what should become of them. Can't you conquer yourself? Surely they did not break your backbone there?" Where do you go every afternoon and evening? Do you need another woman, a younger one, a happier one?"

"No, Victoria, you are — " I said no more; it was not necessary. I waited until we had had our refreshments and had paid; then we started back to the hotel. On the way I told my wife about the dishwashing for the first time. The effect was entirely different from what I had expected. She became extremely angry, beat her head against the wall of a house, cried, and could not be calmed. Finally I succeeded in moving her so far that she returned with me to the little café, which they were about to close. They put the chairs on the tables around us, and we had to pay as soon as we got our drinks.

"Why? Why?" She wept and pushed the two glasses away. "This stuff costs money and we are lacking bread." She took my head by my temples and pulled me close, so that I felt her hot breath. "Didn't you realize that you did not want to take bread from a fat French doctor and therefore had to take scanty bread from a French dishwasher? No, no, no!" She began to laugh shrilly, without a transition. She was in her menopause. Hot flashes of feeling poured over her. I understood her as a doctor. But not as a husband. Now she was in good spirits. She emptied both glasses. I was not thirsty. I pressed her to tell me about the money situation. She continued to laugh and said, "Three hundred thousand francs in gold." Everything I did to urge her to explain herself was in vain. She kept her secrets. I had revealed mine.

I had not stopped looking for peace. Sometimes I hoped that I would find it again with her, whom I had once loved very much. No, not very much, simply loved. But she took from me the little quiet which I had won in the meantime, and I recognized with horror that common misfortune can drive people apart. I no longer differentiated her irony from her seriousness, and soon we stopped talking about serious matters.

I had assumed that von Kaiser would come sometime in the course of 1934. When he did not come and I did not hear from him I was hurt, for I felt a lack, but on the other hand (for I still tried to be fair to both sides of a question) I thought that his health was probably good, for he had proposed to visit me only when he felt himself near death.

My children attended good schools, half French, half German. In the morning an automobile came for them, for children from all over the city attended; in the evening they were brought back. I did not ask anymore where the money came from. Occasionally I had some small casual earnings; I did translations, slowly but carefully, word for word with the greatest accuracy and scrupulousness. While I worked, the children romped around the room, throwing the thick dictionaries at each other, and I marveled that the neighbors did not object. But the children were well liked in the hotel because of their liveliness; everyone gave them something — a bonbon, a ticket to the movie or to the circus — or smiled cordially at them. I was treated seriously, coldly.

As long as I was there, both the children and Victoria were silent about Germany. Whether they talked about their home when I was absent — who could tell? At first the children had favored me — that was still Angelica's influence, which had emphasized their love for me as a hundred per cent Aryan. Soon that too changed, and they were more attached to their mother. For them I was too formal, too controlled. I never hit them, but neither did I caress them.

One day all three came to me, and Lise explained that she had made up her mind about something; Bobby said the same, as did Victoria. I looked up from my work, unsuspecting. Then they all laughed, as if from one throat, and I discovered their secret. My wife had received an offer (through Helmut, who had important French acquaintances) to take charge of the household of a large villa, resembling a castle, near Versailles. She would receive three hundred and fifty francs a month and free living for herself and the children. What good fortune! An official work permit was not necessary.

My daughter could learn housekeeping there. She had other plans for later. She had inherited her mother's gorgeous blond hair. My wife, who wanted to be proud of her beautiful daughter, had taken Lise shortly before to a good salon and had had her hair styled like elegant French adolescent girls'. For days afterward I was supposed to admire the splendor. But it had made no impression on me. I had lived too long in a different world from those three. Lise had discovered real pleasure in her hairdressing. Her heart's desire was to learn it. She was still too young to be apprenticed, but it was not long until I saw how she tried out her skills on the other children in the hotel. She would sit on the stairs above them, hold the child's head between her knees, and with Victoria's comb and brush, which she dampened in a little jar, she would make curls for the patient children. No one asked me about it. My vote scarcely counted, and that was right. How could I have forbidden her?

It was different in Bobby's case. He had the idea of becoming a waiter, either in a café or, better, in a hotel. At one time or another he must have seen in a large exclusive hotel a number of elegant waiters in well-fitting frockcoats and stiff shirts, with manicured hands — I did not learn where, but perhaps it was at Helmut's, who was living very elegantly by then and never invited me. But this vocational choice did not please me. And my wife was supposed to have given her consent lightheartedly? I could not believe it. Our son — a waiter? I tried once more to discuss something. But when I tried to persuade my wife to go to the café again, she did not want to leave her warm bed and held her fingers on her lips, as her sainted father had once done, to keep me silent.

"The children are modern. They know what they are doing. Quiet now! Don't wake them!"

The day for the beginning of my wife's service came. I helped the three pack their possessions but did not go to Versailles with them. Afterward, breathing more easily, I rearranged my room and put my son's bed in the hall. I felt good that I could live alone. I did not have peace yet, but I did have quiet. I economized still more. The thirty marks which came regularly from home were sufficient, since I received enough to eat in the emigrant kitchen. I had grown accustomed to the work there, and had acquired a habit which I had never been able to practice before. I heard people talking, but I shut myself off from it with such force that it was as if they were silent, or as if an automobile passed by, or the gas fire hissed. I had not become blind like *him* but deaf.

My wife soon gave me good reports. The work was not simple, but the surroundings were magnificent. The people had two automobiles, three bathrooms. "Our Lise" had become friendly with the "little princess," the daughter of the house, and had given her a splendid coiffure — although she had torn out a lot of hair in the process. She was silent about my son, and I did not inquire. I began to recuperate physically; the welts on my back became flatter and paler. They would never disappear. Sometimes I thought that Kaiser would never come, and that if he came, he would not recognize me. Both were false. In the summer of 1936 he came to us — Helmut and me — this time without Katinka. He had no thought of dying soon.

Actually, Councillor Gottfried von Kaiser, M.D., was really a miracle. A handsome old man, carrying himself very erect (thanks to a clever corset worn between his skin and shirt), with abundant snow-white hair as well as a full beard (his eyebrows, however, coal black), with restrained movements, dressed to perfection by an English tailor, dignified and enchanting at the same time, surrounded by the finest, somewhat sharp, aromatic perfume like an aura of divinity, at the height of his powers, full of new plans and ideas, ignoring our misery, looking down on our joys, enjoying everything, observing everything, scorning everything — so he appeared in our midst, putting his favorite son Helmut and his favorite pupil in the shade. He was unbroken; he had long since freed himself from the chains which Katinka had shaped and he spoke of her with fairness. She had become heavier with the years, and in conversation he sometimes called her "little doll," sometimes "little fatty." He was looking for a perfume that would be new to her, and he dragged Helmut and me in his big, snow-white automobile, with a coal-black Negro in white summer livery as chauffeur, from one tailor to another with the assertion that it was tailors and not perfume manufacturers who created the most exciting fragrances. After he had bought a sufficient supply, he went to the jewelers' shops in the Place Vendôme, and I, who considered a hundred francs a livelihood, was supposed to help him select an emerald, or ruby, or a black pearl, valued at several tens of thousands — and I did it to the best of my knowledge.

I accompanied him to the suburb of Vincennes, where he was collecting material from the Museum of the World War for his "historical psychiatric studies." He took pleasure in studying these army orders, newspaper clippings and other documents in order to find evidences of individual insanity and mass insanity. He was old and had become wise. He had long ago given up wanting to cure people. He understood them in the essence of their being, found something new in the old, and there was no end to his learning. Instead of anatomical cross sections of the brain, he studied a cross section of Europe at the beginning of the twentieth century. How much I would have liked to give him the little contribution to the history of the mightiest man of our time which fate or coincidence had put into my hands in 1918! But this report did not belong in my hands. My hands had worked disaster. In my overconfident godlikeness I had made a blind man see without giving him regular sleep, that is, peace of the soul. He did not sleep, and just as in the Reserve Hospital in P. he let no one else sleep. In 1918 he had excited only a lounge full of people; in 1936 he did the same for the whole earth.

My master had grasped more clearly than I that the truly upsetting and victorious leaders of people have always been insane. Their hate was not helpless but creative. Their lies did not collapse but shaped all of life around them, as faith does.

Kaiser had come so far that he neither hated nor loved. He felt well because he did not hope or fear anyone. He was afraid only of dying, that is, of pain, not of death. Had he not won this peace after he divorced himself from all that was human? He was thankful for the beautiful evening and did not fear the end.

He weighed the total history of our unhappy fatherland with the true objectivity of the scholar.

I had wanted to be the eyewitness. He was it. For he did not love. His love for Katinka (the only woman to whom he ever really belonged and in whom love was uncovered as slavery) was long dead, since he had learned to see through not only his "little doll" but also himself. As a second La Rochefoucauld, less feudal but also less embittered, he seemed to be eternal in his clarity. Devoted to all achievable pleasures, bowing before the beauty of a new Katinka (whose name he never divulged, speaking only of her "great onyx eyes" and certain exciting secrets of her body), he stood above my ideal of peace, of right, because he demonstrated in his search and in its fulfillment the courage to show himself in an anarchical world to be just as hard and indifferent as the world had become, and so he had the power to let the barbarians on the outside beat at the walls of his tower without opening it to them.

His happiness would have been complete if two seemingly attainable wishes had been granted him. He had hoped to take us both back to Italy with him. Why did he not succeed with Helmut? Did Helmut's "friends" tie him to Paris? I could not believe it. People like them are all over. There was something else. Helmut had a kind of heavy-headed needle stuck in the buttonhole of his jacket. One had to look sharply in order to see in the silver ornaments a tiny swastika. Helmut was therefore less the son of his godlike father and more the disciple of his savior A.H. He had forgiven him the death of R., and was only waiting until A.H. forgave him and permitted him to return to the glorious Third Reich. And I? I felt that something had to be changed. But not by means of the aged god. Kaiser represented my past, a past of glorious development. But he did not free me; he did not give me peace.

When von Kaiser visited me, the great battle in Spain between the republican government and the rebelling generals was already in progress. These generals had the army and a large part of the navy behind them. They were also under the protection of Germany and Italy. They had the help of the higher ecclesiastics and of the powerful landowners, while the mass of the people and the lower clergy were on the side of the Republic. The battle was fought on both sides with the most frightening passion. The Republic had no planes; the rebels received them in vast quantities from Germany and Italy. The rebels were short of manpower and brought Moors and black Berbers into the Catholic country as well as Protestant mercenaries. The rebel troops moved forward to Madrid with unbelievable speed. The capital of the country was enclosed on almost all sides; its fall and with it the destruction of the Republic seemed to be only a question of days. At the beginning of September the border city of Irun fell into the hands of the rebels; there were horrible scenes of murder, arson, of the unleashed satanic soul, beside which the atrocities of the World War paled.

One evening Helmut and I took our leave from von Kaiser. He had not repeated his request that we go to Rome with him. He did not weep. I think that old people weep either very easily or not at all. He belonged to the second kind. He did only one thing. He leaned suddenly over the beautiful marble table at which we sat with whiskey and liqueurs — and there was a strange noise. The corset under his shirt had creaked; it was not made for emotional movements. Helmut smiled about his father. I did not. We were both young compared to him: we were only gray; he, however, was white, twenty-six years older than we. We all said to ourselves that when we separated, and he went back to Rome, it was very unlikely that all three of us would ever see each other again. It was clear to me from hints that Helmut had no other goal than to go to Spain to battle on the side of the victorious generals. Whether or not he came back alive meant little to him. He had never valued life very highly, but he wanted to fight on the side of the stronger, with the prospect of success, and return to the homeland, back in the good graces of the Führer, after he had been so unheroic as to withdraw himself from A.H.'s justice by flight. Helmut, like me, had never been a man of many words. He had always followed his own direction. Inner conflicts were unknown to him, and I am sure that at that table he was the happiest of us three.

Kaiser lived in a palace of a hotel near the Opera House. As Helmut and I continued along the boulevard to the Madeleine, we came to a brilliantly lighted display. But in this display there were neither shoes nor silk lingerie nor furs, neither books nor perfume bottles — nothing but a mass of greatly enlarged photographs and, higher up, a moving tape which gave the latest reports from the Spanish war scene. Helmut stopped, as did I. We read the reports which moved in front of us, word by word. As there was mention of a strategic retreat, Helmut's sullen face grew darker. But how he brightened up when he read the last words; to his joy he discovered that it was not the rebels but the government troops which had begun this little strategic retreat and that this was a republican report.

Then he was pacified; he wanted to move on and was even ready to sit down with me for an hour in a café.

I looked at the photographs on display. The generals did not interest me, nor the people's militia marching in step, nor the miners from Asturias with their open shirts, but I could not turn away from a picture set farther back in a dark corner, of a four- or five-year-old child who had been struck by an aerial bomb and who lay mutilated in his own blood.

"Who's interested in that?" said my friend. I was cruel; I pushed him from me with such force that he fell into the street, almost under a bus.

Terribly agitated, I walked homeward. I paid no attention to Helmut.

But this terror awakened something divine in me, a hope, an illumination, a goal and a final joy in being. I knew all of a sudden that I was not dead in my living body. I was more alive than Kaiser and his son. I wanted to act, to function, no longer to destroy myself. "Help others," I said to myself, "then you'll help yourself; leave God alongside." I breathed easily; I walked quickly and without effort. I climbed the steep streets to Montmartre with the ease of a ten-year-old. I did not sleep much, but I was not sleepless because of a lack of peace as before; I had to stay awake to think about everything to be done the next day and to chart my path exactly, as I had always done.

I had an appointment on the next day with Kaiser. I telephoned him early, too early. He could not understand that I had no time that morning. I could not understand that Katinka, the beauty with the onyx-eyes, and his historic-psychiatric studies were more important to him than what I wanted to tell him. I had thought of the idea that he could go to Spain with me. Whether he died there or in his perfumed palace in Rome — I would not have hesitated. He too did not hesitate. He went to Rome, and his son to Burgos.

I had two decisions to make. The first concerned my resolve to serve in the army in Spain which was loyal to the government. I was not the only one who volunteered. There were still many who thought that the side of the weaker could represent the better thing. I was measured in the truest sense of the word. I am tall and muscular; my gray hair, however, made me appear older than I was. My application was accepted. I was a veteran soldier. I was a veteran military doctor. I had decorations from the old German empire. But what should I be? In which capacity should I serve? How would I serve the good cause best? As a doctor behind the front, as a storm troop leader at the front? I did not hesitate in my heart. I knew exactly where I was drawn. But I left it to fate to decide — that is, the commission at the Spanish General Consulate.

They decided that I could be of greater service as a doctor. They had enough soldiers, but only a few doctors. The total civilian population had shown itself ready to take up weapons and to be trained in their use. The training required only a few weeks, at the most a few months. Afterward a metalworker from the city, a farmer from the country, was a full-fledged soldier. But a doctor cannot be improvised so quickly. I was happy about this decision, signed my name to a form, and learned where and when I should join the next transport over the Pyrenees.

Several people at the consulate had known me before, but I did not get into any long conversations. Instead I hurried home to take care of everything which needed to be done.

I telephoned my wife and asked her to come immediately. She recognized from the tone of my voice that something decisive had happened. She agreed to meet me, but not in Paris, rather in Versailles, because she wanted to lose as little time as possible; she took her work in the house very seriously.

On the way to Versailles, on the little train on the left bank of the Seine, I thought about my second decision. Should I confide in my wife? Should I tell her what I had done and what had made me so happy? Or should I spread a kindly veil over it and imply that I was going "abroad" with my master. That decision was not taken out of my hand, as at the consulate. I had to make it myself. I feared that my decision would destroy the last remnant of our marriage, that she would never forgive me for acting as Leon Lazarus had.

She listened to everything with a deathly pale, distorted face, her eyes downcast, silent. I was brief. Perhaps the format was hard. But if I had been more hesitant to say what I was certain of, I would have only created more damage.

After we had walked silently through the castle park of Versailles for a quarter of an hour, we sat down on a bench and began to talk. I wanted to see my children before I left. In the case of Lise it was easy, but it was more difficult with Bobby, who had obtained a position as an elevator boy in a second-class hotel. My wife remarked rather bitterly that he had had some good fortune — he had not had to change his name since almost all elevator boys were called Bobby. I knew what was behind the irony and acted as if I too found it fortunate. He worked at night and slept until evening. Since I had to leave during the afternoon, he had to be awakened. I found him quite charming in his tight-fitting, brightly colored uniform, almost more so than his sister. They were in no way disturbed by the thought that they would not see me for some time. They looked at their mother, and since she was quiet and self-controlled they were too. I gave them both little presents, which they traded with each other for I had not made the right choice. Then I was alone with my wife.

She avoided speaking about the past or the future. Only once did she raise her clear, cool glance to me, saying, "Now it has been demonstrated how correct I was about the papers. If I had not turned them over, you would long hence have been buried in the camp. Now, however, you can still contribute to an honorable cause."

I answered her, as I took her rough, workworn, reddened hand tight between my hands and caressed it, that everything was all right. If she were satisfied with my decision, I would leave for my work happy, as happy as a person like me could be in such a time. It would be better than washing dishes. And as she started to interrupt me, I said that I understood her and I entrusted the children to her — that was no particular evidence of trust — but I also entrusted her with all my notes: she was to do with them as she wished if I did not return. That reconciled her. I promised to write her as often as possible, to send her my pay, and to think of her always with respect, trust and gratitude — also with such a love as friends hold for each other. Perhaps Helmut would be on the front opposite me in Spain. But she and I would never be enemies. So I remained loyal to her and to myself.

POSTSCRIPT
by Klaus-Peter Hinze

With the years going by, emptiness is growing around me. I am still living, feeling, having desires and hopes. I do not fear death itself, but I dread the hour, when, out of exhaustion, there is no more hope left within me for anything.

DURING A short stay in Paris in 1933, the famous novelist and physician Ernst Weiss wrote these despairing words. A Jew, he was forced to leave Germany after Hitler seized power. Seven years later, on June 14, 1940, when the first German soldiers marched into Paris, he ended his life. His suicide was indeed an ironic tragedy, for he was unaware that through the help of Eleanor Roosevelt and Thomas Mann an immigration visa had already been issued and a ticket to the United States was waiting for him. *"Vive la France quand-même"* were the last words of the farewell letter he left in his shabby hotel room.

Weiss, a German writer of Czechoslovakian nationality, was born in 1882 in Brno, Moravia, into a family of textile merchants. The second of four children, he was five when his father died. Their apparently intelligent and energetic mother, who was ambitious for her children, supervised their education carefully. The eldest, Egon, studied law and became a university professor in Prague. The third son, Otto, also a lawyer, lived in Reichenberg. Ernst and the only daughter, Alice, both became medical doctors.

Ernst studied at the universities of Prague and Vienna, where he attended Sigmund Freud's lectures and made his first contact with psychoanalysis. He specialized in surgery, however, and in 1910 he became an assistant to Emil Theodor Kocher of Berne, one of the outstanding surgeons of his time, who received the Nobel Prize that same year. Kocher was not only Weiss's teacher but also a fatherly friend, and many doctor figures depicted in Weiss's novels were modeled after him. Kocher's requirement that his assistants write medical reports was the first impetus for Weiss to write a novel, and his approach, style, and structure are obviously influenced by the demands of this documentary genre. Because of a slight tuberculosis, Weiss became the doctor on board an Austrian ocean liner and made extensive voyages to Japan, China, and India. During the First World War he served as a regimental doctor in the Austrian army and spent the whole time on the Eastern Front. Two years after the war, like so many of his friends and colleagues — e.g., Ehrenstein, Wolfenstein, Kafka — he moved to Berlin. There he left the medical profession altogether and became a free-lance writer. This decision was by no means ill considered, for he had published several novels, a vast amount of war poetry, and the revolutionary drama *Tanja*. All these works had been highly acclaimed and had won him a respectable name in European literary circles. His major genre became the novel; he wrote more than twenty novels on various topics, of which *The Eyewitness* was his last.

Today the lives of the German emigrants in Paris remain a focus for a certain morbid fascination. Those who are still alive talk even to this day with lowered voices about their constant fear of losing permission to stay in France and being forced to return to Germany and consequent imprisonment in a concentration camp. They recall their financial pressures as well as their interest in politics and feel a personal involvement in world history.

The writers were in a particularly precarious position; they had left behind their readers, their publishers, the magazines and newspapers that had published their works, and thus they lost their source of income. Ernst Weiss had been well known and was considered one of the very best novelists of his time, but the income from his books written in exile could not even partially cover his living expenses. It is heartbreaking to read the letters in which he asked well-to-do friends for financial help. The funds he did receive never lasted longer than one or two months. Through the good offices of Thomas Mann and Stefan Zweig, he received a monthly stipend of thirty dollars from the American Guild for German Cultural Freedom from 1938 on. The few friends who visited him in his tiny, fifth-floor hotel room tell about his deplorable circumstances. Despite a stomach ulcer, he worked at a feverish tempo in order to finish one novel after the other, knowing almost certainly that there was no publisher to print them nor an audience to buy them.

In the summer of 1938, Weiss read the following advertisement in the *Pariser Tageszeitung,* the official newspaper of the German emigrants: "The American Guild for German Cultural Freedom has put at the disposal of the German Academy a literary award for the best German novel by an exiled writer. The American firm Little, Brown & Co. will give this award as advance payment for the American edition of the prize winning novel." The requirements concerning topic and length followed. The manuscript had to be submitted under a pseudonym. The members of the jury were Thomas Mann, Alfred Neumann, Rudolf Olden, Lion Feuchtwanger, and Bruno Frank. Working in great haste, Weiss wrote *The Eyewitness* in less than two months and submitted it shortly before the deadline of October 1.

This novel about a doctor contains elements of autobiography, and as such it is typical of Ernst Weiss's earlier oeuvre. Surprisingly new, however, is his coming to terms with the current political problems and his including himself as an "eyewitness" of his time and age. His political involvement is in sharp contrast to the psychological and medical orientation expressed in previous works. Until the end of the 1920s, Weiss was an apolitical man and artist. With the rise of fascism, however, he realized that he had to relinquish such a position. In 1928 President Hindenburg personally gave him the silver medal of the Olympiade for his work *Boëtius von Orlamünde,* an educational novel with a socialist message, and that same year he started to write his first political work, a novel on the rise of fascism. Other literary plans and his subsequent departure from Berlin were responsible for the fact that this novel, of which two thirds were written, was never finished. To the best of our knowledge no manuscript remains.

In the summer of 1933 Weiss met Dr. Edmund Forster, the psychiatrist who committed suicide a few weeks later under pressure from the Nazi regime; this meeting had a decisive impact on Weiss's life, for he had become privy to a psychological phenomenon that for him explained the metamorphosis of Private First Class "A.H." into Germany's Führer. Anyone who has read *The Eyewitness* cannot doubt that at that time Weiss read Forster's medical report of the soldier "A.H.," who had been a patient in the hospital at Pasewalk in 1918.

The political situation did not permit Weiss to use Forster's material as the basis for a novel. "No publishing house in Europe would print such a political novel," he admitted in a letter to the American Guild. Indeed, such a publication would have seriously endangered all the German refugees in France as well as the few remaining free publishing houses and newspapers. It might even have put Dr. Forster's widow and children into the hands of the Gestapo. The material had to remain unused. In any case, whether or not the publication of it would have made any impact on the political situation is highly questionable. The great majority of the German people wanted Hitler as their Führer, their dictator. Ernst Weiss recognized that. While he was working on *The Eyewitness,* he wrote an aphorism on the subject of the relationship between a dictator and the masses: "If anyone tries to unmask the dictator he will have little success with the stupid mass of people. Because when the masses in their suspicion and stupidity give their trust to one individual, they hold on to him as long as possible. Inertia is their form of loyalty."

So Weiss did not immediately use the explosive material, but instead turned to the past. "What else is there left to us writers in exile but to nourish our memories and write memoirs?" he said at the PEN Congress in Paris in 1939. His own strongest allegiances were to the society of the Austro-Hungarian monarchy. Rudolf Olden, much younger than Weiss, is said to have replied: "We will write our memoirs once we have returned from exile; now our interest and energy belong to the present and to the future." This was typical of the younger generation of writers.

Many of Weiss's friends from Prague and Berlin had made their political beliefs public and had committed themselves to socialism. Weiss had delved into socialist ideas, but found them in conflict with his belief in individualism. His "great master," as he called Thomas Mann, had come into the open after some hesitation and announced his decision to fight Hitler and fascism. Weiss wrote to Mann: "I admire your position more than ever. You give to us others, who are so much weaker than you, an example of indomitable heroism of the spirit that opposes the insanity of violence, even though the latter may seem victorious at the moment." Mann's example, as well as the demands of the day and the chance to win a prize in the Guild's competition, reactivated his former plans for a political novel based on the material dealing with Hitler's psychoanalysis. The novel was written and sent to New York under the pseudonym "Gottfried von Kaiser." Some people at the Guild encouraged him to think it might win, and several of the competition's judges recommended it for publication. In the end, though, *The Eyewitness* was rejected. An unknown writer, Arnold Bender, was awarded the prize.

Weiss knew that because of the pressure of the deadline he had not structured the novel to satisfy his own rigorous standards. When he thought that he might win the contest, he wrote to the Guild: "I would like to inform you that in the meantime I have considerably restructured this novel and essentially deepened its artistic message. The first version I sent you was composed in too short a time for it to meet my own standards. I believe that half a year's serious work on *The Eyewitness* has been successful." Later, he also changed the title, to *The Fools' Emperor,* thereby indicating a shift of emphasis in the novel. Under the title *The Eyewitness,* he had stressed the narrator's, the doctor's role. In the new version he emphasized Hitler's position, making him "the fools' emperor." (The fact that two of the older doctors in the novel also bear the name "Kaiser," and that Weiss had chosen the pseudonym "Gottfried von *Kaiser,*" i.e., "emperor," is typical of his leaning toward symbolism.) It has not been possible to find out what ever happened to the revised manuscript, which in Weiss's view bore his full artistic message.

At the time of Weiss's suicide, Paris was occupied by the German army and terrorized by the Gestapo, and all of his manuscripts, including the diaries which he believed to be his literary masterpiece, were lost or destroyed. That the first version of *The Eyewitness* survived is owed to a lucky circumstance. Many years after the Second World War, Paul Gordon, a publisher of plays, found it in New York, and offered it to several newspapers and publishing houses in West Berlin and West Germany. He claimed, without being able to prove anything, that the novel portrayed actual historical events. One publisher after another declined the work.

Finally, in 1963, the young Hermann Kreisselmeier published the novel simply as a work of fiction, a novel by a forgotten but once celebrated writer. The publication did not basically influence Hitler's biography. Until the results of Rudolph Binion's research were published, Hitler's own version of his blindness caused by mustard gas was never doubted. In 1938, when Weiss wrote his novel, he could not comprehend the tremendous consequences of Dr. Forster's "miracle cure" of Hitler. Only in restrospect is it possible to understand the importance of what Weiss describes, barely disguised as fiction. These new facts contribute to a fresh understanding of the history of the twentieth century and Adolf Hitler, the man who exerted such a tremendous influence on the destiny of Germany and the world.

Ernst Weiss's novels *Georg Letham, Arzt und Mörder; Boëtius von Orlamünde; Der Gefängnisarzt; Der Verführer;* or *Der arme Verschwender* — just to mention a few — are unknown in the English-speaking world; they form a striking counterpoint and parallel to the works of his celebrated friend, Franz Kafka.

Ernst Weiss's greatest desire was to publish novels in the United States. Thirty-seven years after his death this desire is being granted through the present publication.